SNAKES

ACKNOWLEDGMENTS

The book concept was introduced to me by Hervé Tardy of Copyright S.A.R.L., and I thank him for his faith in the project. My very good friend Donald Strydom, owner of Swadini Reptile Park and Nelspruit Reptile World, went out of his way to make his facilities available as well as tracked down scarce snakes that I still needed to photograph. Donald accommodated and fed us while also assisting with rather long and painful photographic sessions.

Some of the photographs were taken at Transvaal Snake Park, and I thank Dave Morgan, who, as in the past, was more than willing to assist.

My sincere thanks to Tom Crutchfield of Tom Crutchfield's Reptile Enterprises, Inc., in Bushnell, Florida, for making his extensive collection available to photograph, and David Fowler for his help and patience. Bill Love of Glades Herpetofauna, Inc., in Fort Myers, Florida, made his facilities available and also provided me with many excellent photographs for the book. I also, as so often in the past, relied on Paul and Deanne Moler for help, a bed to sleep in, and food to eat. They went out of their way to make my visit to Florida a pleasant and successful one.

Crawford Coulson accommodated me in England and tracked down some of the more difficult-to-find European snakes. Another very good friend, whom I had not seen in eleven years, John Pickett, located most of the European snakes that I needed to photograph and then went to considerable trouble and expense to help me photograph them. Thanks also to Stephen Peltz for making his photographic studio available.

A number of people either helped track down photographs or made photographs available. Thanks to Bill Love of Glades Herpetofauna, Inc., Rick Mathews, Peter Dawson, John Thornbjarnarson, Dr. Sherman Minton, Rom Whitaker, Dr. Bill Branch, Wayne Van Deventer, William Holmstrom, Craig Forbes, and Paul Moler.

Last but by no means least, my thanks to my friends and family for their support. It is not possible to name everyone who helped with the book in various ways, but to all of them I say thank you. I have always enjoyed a great deal of support from my father and my good friend Gerrie Smith. The biggest thanks goes to my wife, Molleen, and daughter Melissa. They had to live with my working late at night, being extremely frustrated at times, or otherwise away from home, and throughout this period I received a lot of love, encouragement, and support from them.

Original title: *L'Univers fascinant des Serpents*
Published by Éditions Solar—Paris, France
© 1994 Copyright Studio—Paris, France

This edition published by Barnes & Noble, Inc., by arrangement with Copyright S.A.R.L.

1997 Barnes & Noble Books

Editorial consultant, Jim Breheny
Text composition and redesign by Tony Meisel

ISBN 0-7607-0417-1

Printed in Spain

97 98 99 00 01 M 9 8 7 6 5 4 3 2 1

Bookprint

SNAKES

JOHAN MARAIS

BARNES
&NOBLE
BOOKS
NEW YORK

A Royal Python (Python regius) *with its head to the right, coiled up with an Angolan Dwarf Python* (P. anchietae).

CONTENTS

Introduction

I caught my first snake at the age of nine. While clearing some building rubble in the back of our property in Durban on the east coast of South Africa, I came across a 30 cm (12 in) brown snake.

The snake was terrified and coiled into a defensive position, striking viciously, even though it was perfectly harmless. It took me several minutes to coax the snake into a wooden box. At that stage I had no idea what type of snake it was. I proudly told my parents of my catch but in vain, as my mother ordered me to kill the serpent. The snake was released onto an open patch of grass and I chopped it in half with a large knife. I can still remember the mouth separated from the rest of the body, desperately gasping for air.

In subsequent years I had many encounters with snakes, and I got to know more and more about them. My school holidays were spent with friends and relatives on farms, where I came across and captured several snakes. I would take the snakes to the local snake park for identification, and occasionally the owner of the snake park would pay me for snakes that were of particular interest to him. This became quite a lucrative hobby, and eventually I started looking for snakes in order to earn pocket money.

It took us about an hour on our bicycles to reach our favorite collecting spot on the outskirts of Durban. In the mornings many snakes, including large Black Mambas, leave their hideouts in deep rock crevices or holes in the ground to spend time basking in the sun. Black Mambas often feed on rock hyrax, an abundant small mammal that inhabits rocky areas and lives in large colonies. After such a meal, the mamba spends most of the day coiled up on a rock or in the branches of a low shrub sunning itself, with a visible bulge in its body indicating that it has been successful in obtaining a meal. The Black Mamba is one of the deadliest snakes in the world. Adults average 3 to 4 m (10 to 13 ft) in length. It possesses large quantities of a deadly, fast-acting neurotoxic venom, and its prey is usually killed within minutes. While slowly walking through long grass in search of basking mambas, we could virtually hear one another's heartbeats. It was a terrifying but lucrative experience, as we used to earn about U.S. $3 per foot. A large mamba sold for U.S. $30, at the time the price of a good second-hand bicycle.

My interest in snakes developed as I grew older, and I was often called upon to remove snakes from gardens and houses, bird aviaries, high-rise buildings, and even shopping malls. At the age of twenty-two, after serving five years in the police force, I joined a snake park as an assis-tant.

I had a great deal to learn, as did my employer, and the procedures we followed for the safe handling of venomous snakes on a daily basis left much to be desired.

Within six months of embarking on my new career, I was bitten by a number of venomous snakes, including the Black Mamba, the African Tree Snake, the Cape Cobra, and the Rinkhals. I ended up in intensive care in hospitals no less than four times. I also managed to get snake venom into my eyes several times. Fortunately, I recovered fully from all the bites without any ill effects or permanent damage and never received antivenom serum.

It was, however, only fairly recently that the danger of snakebites really dawned on me. While working on a farm in the majestic Valley of a Thousand Hills in South Africa, a young colleague, Crawford Coulson, was bitten on the lower calf by a large Black Mamba. He got to me within a few minutes and told me how it had happened. He was walking along a footpath when the Black Mamba, which we presume had been asleep, was frightened and bit into his leg. Mamba venom is very fast acting and affects the nervous system.

I immediately asked Crawford how he was feeling,

and he replied that he already had numbness in his lips. We were about 50 km (31 mi) from the closest hospital, and I quickly loaded him into my car and drove off to the hospital at high speed. Amazingly, Crawford was quite relaxed, as he knew that I am an authority on snakes and snakebites. Not that my knowledge was much help, as I was merely driving. Within ten minutes he experienced severe difficulty in breathing and was sweating profusely. I was driving over 200 km/h (125 mi/h) most of the time and had the emergency lights of my car flashing in an attempt to keep the road clear of other vehicles. After twenty minutes, at which stage I was driving through Saturday morning peak traffic, Crawford started losing consciousness. We reached the hospital within thirty minutes of his being bitten, and by that time Crawford was unconscious and close to death.

About half a dozen doctors and nurses battled for more than four hours to keep him alive. Amazingly, he recovered fully and was back at work within two weeks.

Snakes and Humans

A snake charmer with an Indian Cobra (Naja naja).
Contrary to popular belief, the snake does not react to the music
but rather to the swaying movement of the charmer.

Throughout the ages humans have regarded snakes as slimy, repulsive, and aggressive creatures that will harass and attack at every opportunity. In ancient times snakes were worshipped as gods of evil and of death. They were hated, feared, and revered. People have always exaggerated the attributes of snakes, increasing their power and invariably making them larger than life. Even today, many people feel faint if they encounter a snake, while others cannot even look at one in print or on television.

Snakes feature prominently in the Bible. Eve picked fruit from the forbidden tree after being persuaded to do so by the Devil in the guise of a snake. The snake assured her that she would not die but that her eyes would open and she, like God, would know good from evil. She ate of the forbidden fruit and passed some on to Adam. He also ate, and mankind was doomed to sin and death from that day onward. The snake received its own punishment. "And the Lord God said unto the serpent, because thou hast done this, thou art cursed above all cattle, and above every beast of the field: upon thy belly shalt thou go, and dust shalt thou eat all the days of thy life" (Genesis 3:14).

In Exodus 7:1-12, Moses and Aaron had to perform a miracle in front of Pharaoh. Aaron cast his rod down before Pharaoh, and it became a serpent. In Numbers 21:5-9, Moses had led his people into the desert in Egypt. Many of the people spoke against God, complaining because they had no food or water. The Lord then sent serpents among the people, and many of them were bitten and succumbed. They soon asked for forgiveness.

But it is not just in the Bible that snakes are often mentioned. The serpent was also a symbol of Satan, the Egyptian god Ra, and Apollo. Among the Greek Dionysian cults, snakes were regarded as a symbol of fertility and wisdom. During the time of the Roman Empire, snakes kept in special chambers were cared for and fed by vestal virgins. If a snake refused food, it was evidence that its keeper was no longer a virgin and she was sentenced to death. Indians, Burmese, and Siamese regarded the snake as both a demigod and a semidemon. According to legend, Buddha received the wisdom of true Buddhism from the king of serpents, thought to have been the King Cobra (*Ophiophagus hannah*).

Few people in the world were not, in some way or another, affected by snakes. Earliest humans made pictures of snakes by smearing serpent images onto the damp clay walls of their caves in France and Spain. The diminutive nomadic San (Bushmen) of southern Africa painted fine examples of snakes on rocks. Today, the few surviving San still hunt snakes for food. In Australia, the snake also featured fairly often in the paintings of the Aborigines.

People were and still are fascinated by snakes. This may be because of its ability to appear and disappear in what may be perceived to be a magical way, while others associate the snake with dead ancestors, spirits, and even the netherworld. Its ability to shed its skin has led to the belief that it can revive itself, providing new life and strength.

In recent years plentiful fallacies have created more confusion. Probably the most popular fallacy, and one of the main reasons why people do not like snakes, is that they are wet and slimy. Snakes often have shiny skins that may look wet and slimy but are, in fact, perfectly dry and pleasant to touch. Like many fishermen, people invariably exaggerate the size and thickness of any snake they may encounter. Have you not heard of the snake that stretched from one side of the road to the other, its head disappearing while the tail had not yet emerged on the other side? Another favorite fallacy is that snakes drink milk from cows. This fallacy may well have originated when farm laborers stole milk by milking cows without the knowledge of the farmer and blamed snakes. Snakes do not have the ability to suck and cannot drink large volumes of liquid. In the wild, snakes never drink milk. They also have numerous sharp teeth that would upset any cow, should a snake attempt to drink milk from her. The Loop Snake supposedly places its tail in its mouth to form a loop and then rolls down hills, chasing people or prey. On the subject of chasing people, there are also many supposed instances of snakes' chasing after people on horseback. Snakes do not chase after people and cannot achieve high speeds. The maximum speed of a fast-moving snake, over a short distance, is probably less than 15 km/h (9 mi/h). Because snakes lack eyelids and always appear to be staring, they are thought to be able to hypnotize their prey and even humans. This fallacy was fueled by stories such as *The Jungle Book*. Another fallacy is that should one not consume salt from birth, the venom of any dangerous snake will not cause any harm.

The interesting fact about humans' fear of snakes is that children up to the age of three have no innate fear of snakes and enjoy playing with them. It is only at the age of about four, once their parents or peers begin to tell them about snakes, that they develop a fear. The fear of snakes, to a large degree, is based on a lack of knowledge. People know very little about snakes and seldom understand and appreciate these fascinating creatures.

Eve with the forbidden fruit, and the evil serpent that was successful in tempting her.

THE ORIGIN OF SNAKES

The origin of snakes is still something of a mystery, largely because paleontologists have little material to work with. Because snakes have very fine ribs and bones, and a delicate skull, relatively few fossils have been found. The forces of nature destroyed most of the evidence that littered the earth through the years.

The first reptiles appeared in the Upper Carboniferous Period, some 300 million years ago. In evolutionary time it was quite a sudden phenomenon that may, to some extent, have resulted from dramatic climatic changes that took place at the time. Swamps dried up in intense heat, profoundly affecting amphibious forms of life.

Herbivores had not yet evolved in the Early Permian Period, roughly 260 to 280 million years ago, and reptiles preyed on one another. Many reptiles evolved at the time, and it is believed that the first lizards appeared about 250 million years ago. The first paramammals then evolved, some of them covered in fur. Their reign was short-lived, as the rise of the dinosaurs in the Triassic and Jurassic Periods led to their demise. These giant reptiles dominated the earth for the next 140 million years and eventually died out toward the end of the Cretaceous Period. The reason for their extinction is still not known, despite a great deal of speculation.

It was during the Cretaceous Period that the first ancestors of snakes made their appearance. Snake fossils from that time have been found in North Africa. Although an Algerian fossil, believed to be one of the oldest, dates back 100 million years, there is little doubt that the first snakes appeared during the Lower Cretaceous Period, some 135 million years ago, and perhaps even during the Upper Jurassic Period, which stretches back 135 to 155 million years.

Many snakes that existed when dinosaurs roamed and ruled the earth were probably not much different in size from those that live today. Huge pythonlike snakes measuring 15 m (49 ft) or more disappeared at the beginning of the Tertiary Period. The snake world was dominated by smaller pythonlike snakes during the first two-thirds of the Tertiary Period, some 23 to 65 million years ago.

Colubrid snakes first appeared toward the beginning of the Tertiary Period, some 35 to 53 million years ago. Then the climate cooled dramatically in the Miocene Period, about 20 million years ago, and the giant snakes withdrew from their northernmost range. The first viperlike snake, according to fossil records, made its appearance at the beginning of the Miocene Period, 21 to 23 million years ago, while the first elapid appeared as recently as 18 million years ago, much later in the Miocene Period. There is some speculation that the colubrid snakes were all venomous but lost their venom during millions of years of evolution.

Most scientists agree that snakes evolved from burrowing lizards, but the "missing link" still has to be found to substantiate such a theory. It is believed that they first lost their limbs, as limbs were no longer necessary underground. In fact, they would have been quite a handicap. The ears went next, as they would have clogged up with dirt. Instead, certain bones in the ear were linked to the jaw, thereby enabling snakes to "sense" sound, especially strong vibrations. Lastly, there was no use for eyes underground, and they disappeared. Once snakes took to the surface, their eyes were required and reappeared.

Even today some snakes, like the pythons and boas, have remnants of hind legs—evidence that they once had limbs. These vestigial hind limbs are visible in the form of spurlike protrusions situated at the base of the tail.

Today there are close to 2,400 species of snake distributed throughout most of the world. They are found in a wide variety of habitats, from deserts to tropical rain forests and the depths of the ocean.

The 10,000-year-old fossil of a ratsnake (Elaphe obsoleta) *discovered in Florida. This fossil was photographed at the Florida Museum of Natural History.*

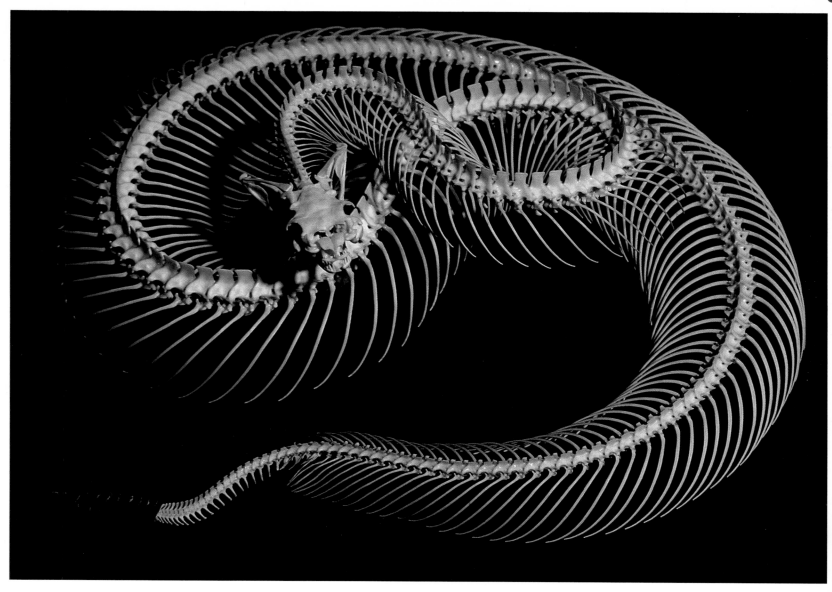

The skeleton of an Eastern Diamondback Rattlesnake (Crotalus adamanteus) *in striking position.*

The Life and Death of Snakes

HIBERNATION

Snakes are often referred to as being cold-blooded, but the term *poikilothermic* is more correct. This does not mean that their blood is cold, but rather, that they have no internal mechanism to control their own body temperature and are dependent on their immediate environment to provide the heat necessary for active metabolism and movement.

In areas where there is a marked difference in temperature between summer and winter, especially the temperate regions, snakes will go into hibernation for as long as cold conditions prevail. Throughout summer they feed voraciously, building up fat reserves for the coming winter. In autumn many snakes spend more time basking, enjoying the last periods of sunshine before going into hibernation. Communal hibernation sites, commonly referred to as dens, may be utilized by snakes of many different species, including both venomous and harmless ones. Such dens may house thousands of snakes,

resulting in masses of snakes slithering about just prior to hibernation. During hibernation they live off accumulated body fat; snakes that have insufficient fat reserves do not survive through winter. Contrary to popular belief, these snakes do not necessarily sleep throughout the winter but are immobile because of the cold. A snake's heartbeat and rate of breathing slow down until they almost stop, depending on the temperature in the den. Should the snake select a den that is not well insulated and the temperature drops below 4°C (39°F), it may well die.

Throughout hibernation snakes show very little, if any, activity. However, on a warm winter's day, a snake may bask near its hideout. Most snakes hibernate in animal holes, beneath rocks, in deep crevices, or even in deserted termite mounds. Once they emerge

from hibernation, snakes often remain close to their dens and will quickly go underground if there is a sudden drop in temperature. Most snakes shed their skins after hibernating; mating

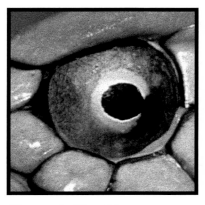

The eye of a King Cobra (Ophiophagus hannah) *with its round pupil.*

may take place soon after that.

Hot weather is as dangerous to snakes as cold, and they may estivate by retreating into underground hideouts. They also do this in times of extreme drought, when water is not available.

After spotting its prey, a Mangrove Pit Viper (Trimeresurus purpureomaculatus) *coils into an S shape, ready to strike.*

VISION

Snakes have good vision but tend to ignore stationary objects. I have often seen a snake chasing after a toad. The moment the toad freezes, the snake loses sight of it and starts searching franti-

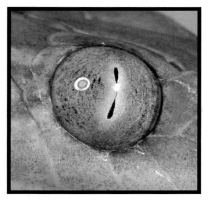

Note the vertical pupil of the nocturnal Brown House Snake (Lamprophis fuliginosus).

cally. Hence the old but true saying that should you come across a snake in the wild, the best thing to do is to stand perfectly still until it has slithered off.

Snakes that are active in the day tend to have round pupils, whereas those that hunt at night have elliptical pupils, like cats and crocodiles. The elliptical pupil can open very wide and, at night, will allow the maximum amount of light to enter the eye.

Snakes that are active in the day (diurnal snakes) usually have the ability to see color, whereas those that hunt at night (nocturnal snakes) cannot see color.

As snakes do not have movable eyelids, they cannot close their eyes. The eye is covered by a transparent piece of skin, called the brille or spectacle, that comes off during shedding.

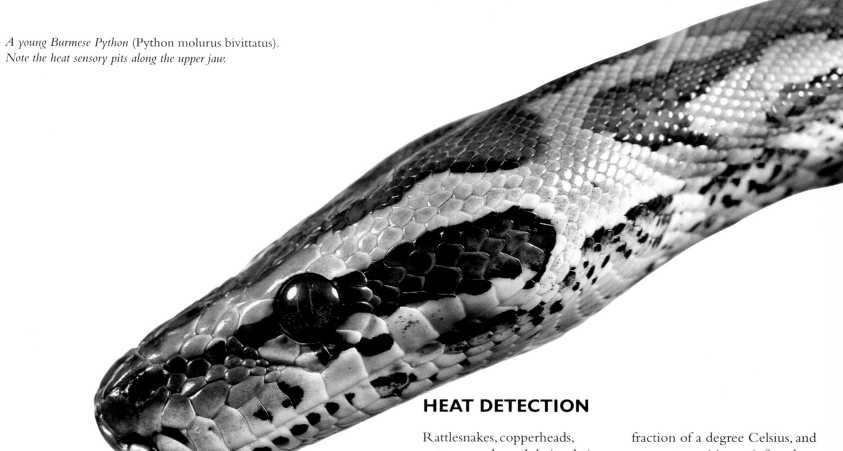

A young Burmese Python (Python molurus bivittatus).
Note the heat sensory pits along the upper jaw.

HEAT DETECTION

Rattlesnakes, copperheads, cottonmouths and their relatives, pit vipers, pythons, and boas have thermoreceptors or heat sensory pits. In pit vipers and their relatives, the pits are situated between the eyes and nostrils and are clearly visible as depressions. Pythons and boas, on the other hand, have heat sensory pits on the upper lips, and these are visible as depressions or slits.

Heat sensory pits are very effective at sensing minute changes in temperature, even a fraction of a degree Celsius, and are most sensitive to infrared rays. This enables the snake to detect warm-blooded prey in pitch darkness. Quite often a rodent may be concealed among vegetation, and it will be invisible to most predators. The heat sensory pits of a snake, however, do not just help the snake locate the rodent but even provide it with an image of the rodent. The snake is then able to strike accurately and effectively and seize its prey without even having seen it!

SMELL

The forked tongue of a snake is harmless and cannot sting or hurt in any way. It is only used for smelling, and snakes have an excellent sense of smell. The tongue is pushed through a groove in the front of the mouth and samples the environment. When it is drawn back into the mouth, the various particles that were picked up are deposited onto an organ in the roof of the mouth known as the Jacobson's organ. These particles are analyzed, and the snake receives a good indication of what is present in its immediate environment.

A Western Diamondback Rattlesnake (Crotalus atrox) *flicks its tongue.*
Note the heat sensory pit between its eye and the tip of its snout.

SCALES

The body of a snake is protected by a skin consisting of water-proof scales. These scales help to conserve water and protect the snake against attack and diseases. Scales vary in shape and size, depending on the species. Boas and pythons have numerous small scales, while most vipers have strongly keeled scales that may overlap. Cobras and mambas, on the other hand, have large, smooth scales. Arboreal snakes often have keeled scales on the belly, and these may assist them in climbing up rough surfaces or into trees. Keeled scales have a raised ridge running down their center. The belly scales, referred to as ventral scales, consist of large, rectangular segments and function in movement.

Most adders and vipers, as well as some other snakes, have strongly keeled scales.

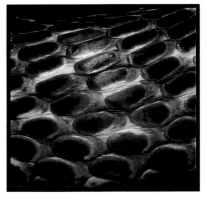

Cobras and mambas, as well as some other snakes, have smooth scales.

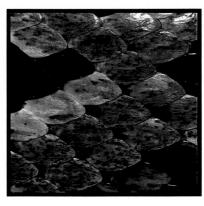

Most pythons and boas have large, smooth scales.

SHEDDING

The outer layer of a snake's skin does not grow, and as it wears and becomes damaged, it is shed. It loosens from the inner, new layer of skin, which is virtually identical to the old skin. The number of times that a snake sheds in a year depends on a variety of factors.

Juvenile snakes, which grow rapidly, may shed up to fifteen times a year, whereas adults may only shed two or three times per year. If the skin of a snake is damaged, it sheds much sooner than usual.

The whole process of shedding may take two weeks. The first sign that a snake is about to shed is that its eyes become a milky-white color, often referred to as the snake's going opaque. This cloudiness takes about ten days to clear. Soon thereafter, the snake rubs its nose against a rough surface to loosen the old skin. It then literally crawls through the mouth of the old skin, which comes off like an inverted sock. It may take a few hours to shed from the moment that the skin

comes loose on the head. The snake's colors are at their best immediately after shedding.

There are specific times that snakes tend to shed their skins. Most do so soon after hibernating. Gravid females usually shed their skins just prior to laying eggs.

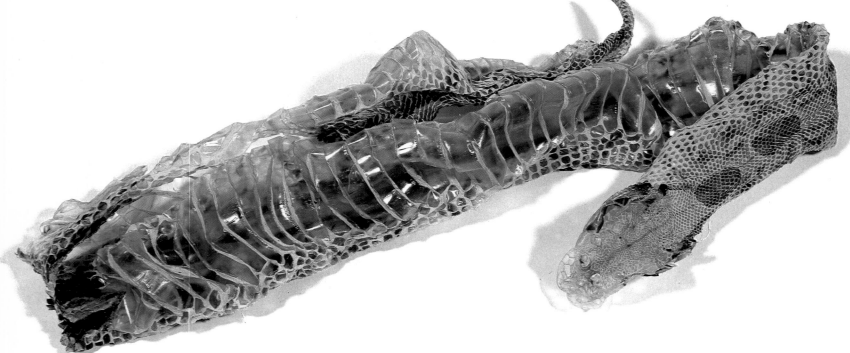

The complete shed skin of a Gaboon Viper (Bitis gabonica).

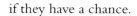

DEFENSES

Snakes fend for themselves in a variety of ways. Many rely on excellent camouflage to remain undetected, while others choose to escape. Some even feign death, only to strike out quickly if they have a chance.

Few snakes stand their ground when danger looms, but the King Cobra of Asia is reputedly one of them, especially in the breeding season.

A threatened cobra that does not choose to flee invariably lifts its head off the ground and spreads a hood. This is done to make the snake look larger than it is. Some cobras are even able to spit their venom and do so effectively over more than 2 m (7 ft). The venom that is spat is the same that the snake would inject if it were to bite. On a person's skin the venom cannot do any harm, but in the eyes it causes severe pain and irritation, resulting in temporary blindness. This gives the snake time to escape.

Other venomous snakes, and even some harmless ones, inflate their necks when threatened, and in doing so may expose vividly colored skin, not usually seen, between the scales. While doing so, some snakes open their mouths aggressively and may even hiss.

Rattlesnakes retain a portion of dry skin on the end of the tail with every shedding. When the tail is vibrated, these pieces of skin, or "rattles," cause a loud rattling sound. This is usually more than enough to scare off most animals and even humans.

Above. *A Mozambique Spitting Cobra* (Naja mossambica) *spits its venom at an aggressor. It is also displaying its hood in self-defense.*

Left. *A new segment on the tail of a rattlesnake forms each time the snake sheds its skin. The rattle may break off from time to time.*

COLOR

Snakes vary dramatically in coloration from species to species and from country to country. While many snakes are rather dull, others are beautifully colored, sometimes even garishly so. These colors may change throughout the life of a snake; juveniles are often more brightly colored than their parents. Mole snakes of the genus *Pseudaspis* are plain and vary in color from black to brown, orange-brown, or light brown, whereas their young have bright zigzag markings with spots and mottles. Color variation is common within species, making it extremely difficult to identify snakes. The African Tree Snake, or Boomslang (*Dispholidus typus*), is an excellent example. Adult males are usually bright green with distinct black interstitial skin. In some areas they are dark brown to black above with a bright yellow belly, or black above with a dark gray belly. Brick red specimens are also found from time to time. Females are light to olive brown with dirty white to brown bellies. The juveniles are brightly colored with brown heads and vivid yellow to orange throats. They also have massive, bright emerald eyes. Color variation is also common in the deadly Cape Cobra (*Naja nivea*) from South Africa, which varies from jet black to shiny brown, or bright orange with darker mottles, or bright yellow. Juveniles have a dark, broad band on the throat.

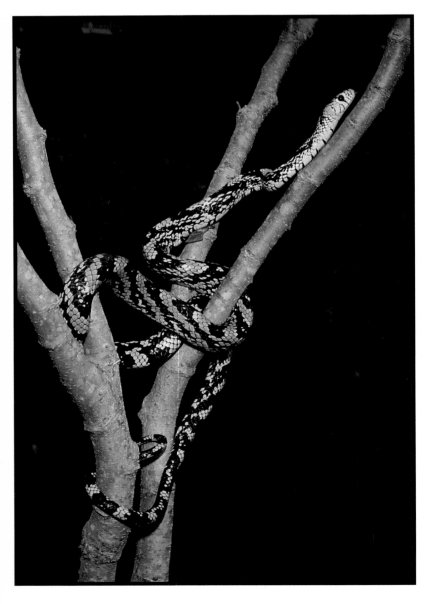

COLORS FOR CONCEALMENT

Snakes, like many other creatures, prefer to avoid confrontation because of the risks involved. Many species have therefore evolved colors that blend in well with their environment. Arboreal snakes, such as the African Green Mamba (*Dendroaspis angusticeps*), are often plain green, which enables them to disappear among the leaves of trees and shrubs. Others, like the Emerald Tree Boa (*Corallus caninus*) of South America, are predominantly green but with some other markings; they, too, are well camouflaged. Desert inhabitants often have a dull color that matches the substrate where they occur. One of the best examples of camouflage in snakes is the African Vine Snake (*Thelotornis* sp.), also known as the Twig Snake. Not only is its body the exact color, complete with markings, of a twig in the wild, but it is also long and slender like a twig or vine in the African bush. This snake is extremely difficult to see. The beautifully colored Gaboon Viper (*Bitis gabonica*), with its mosaic markings in pastel shades, disappears among the leaf litter on the jungle floor but, like many other cryptically colored snakes, appears to have rather bizarre colors when removed from its natural surroundings. While many well-camouflaged snakes remain motionless throughout most of the day to avoid detection, others rely on their camouflage to avoid being seen when they move about in search of food.

A colorful Tiger Ratsnake (Spilotes pullatus) forages for food in its tropical environment.

The Emerald Tree Boa (Corallus caninus) *may appear to be very colorful but is perfectly camouflaged among the leaves of a tree.*

MIMICRY

As do many forms of wildlife, harmless snakes often mimic the colors and habits of dangerous snakes in the hope that they will successfully escape predators. The kingsnakes and milksnakes of the genus *Lampropeltis* mimic the poisonous coral snakes (*Micrurus* sp.) of the Americas. Both snakes commonly have bands of red, black, and yellow and in some areas are often found together, sometimes even under the same rock. In most coral snakes the red bands tend to touch the yellow bands, whereas in the milksnakes the red bands usually touch the black bands.

In Africa, the harmless Rhombic Egg-eater (*Dasypeltis scabra*) mimics the poisonous Night Adder (*Causus rhombeatus*). It has very similar rhombic markings and even has a V marking on its neck, not unlike that on the head of the Night Adder. The interior of the mouth of the Night Adder is black and is exposed when the snake is threatened. The only other African snake that exposes a similar dark mouth interior is the deadly Black Mamba (*Dendroaspis polylepis*).

Harmless green bush snakes of the genus *Philothamnus* are often found in the same habitat as the Green Mamba (*Dendroaspis angusticeps*). People often confuse these harmless snakes for the deadly Green Mamba, but whether it is actually mimicry or purely a camouflage is debatable.

WARNING COLORS

Rather than become involved in conflict and risk injury, some snakes have developed warning colors, a method that is well known among many different creatures in nature. Such colors are common among insects, poisonous fish, marine invertebrates, amphibians, and plants. The poison-arrow frogs of South America are vividly colored in combinations of black and bright green, red, yellow, and even blue.

The coral snakes (*Micrurus* sp.) of the Americas are the best-known species that possess warning colors. They make use of rings of bright red, yellow, or white, and black to brown or gray. For such colors to be effective as a warning, the snakes have to be exposed to predators during the day, when their colors are clearly visible, and the threatening predators must be daylight active. The warning colors of a coral snake will be useless at scaring off predatory owls at night.

LOCOMOTION

Despite appearing to be handicapped by having no limbs and an elongated body, snakes have the ability to go anywhere a legged creature goes—on the ground, underground, in trees, or even in water.

There are many ways in which a snake moves; some are described below.

Serpentine Movement. This is commonly used by most snakes, especially when disturbed or when searching for a potential meal. The snake moves with typical S curves of its body. The body undulates from side to side, with the outer edges of the curves making contact with irregularities on the ground, pushing the body forward in the direction that the snake wants to go. This mode of progression is very effective when the snake is moving through undergrowth or across rocky terrain. The longer the snake, provided it is slender, the more effectively it will move.

Caterpillarlike Movement. Heavy-bodied snakes, such as the Gaboon Viper, Puff Adder, and large pythons and boas, usually move in this manner, unless disturbed. The large belly scales, which overlap like roof tiles, are moved fractionally forward by pairs of ribs and then fractionally backward, creating a caterpillarlike movement. The snake progresses very slowly and in a seemingly straight line. This form of movement has been compared with a child in a sack race, with the legs resembling ribs and the sack the skin of the snake. Picture a long row of kids in a sack race and you will have some idea of how snakes move in this fashion.

Side-winding. A few North American and African desert snakes have adapted to moving about in the desert in what is

A Desert Side-winder (Bitis peringueyi) *side-winds across the warm desert sand by throwing its body sideways, leaving its characteristic track in the process.*

referred to as a side-winding motion. The snake raises its head and the forepart of its body off the ground and throws it sideways at a right angle to the direction that the snake is facing. Before its head touches the ground, the posterior half of the body follows and the snake virtually "walks" sideways, with only two sections of the body touching the ground at any one time. It leaves behind a discontinuous parallel set of tracks. One advantage of this way of progression is that little of the snake's body makes contact with the hot desert sand.

Concertina-type Movement. This way of moving is very slow but often necessary. The snake will extend its body and anchor its head, then drag the rest of the body closer. This may be seen when a snake in a tree has to negotiate a smooth branch.

Burrowing. Certain snakes have adapted to a life underground where they need to burrow in order to find food and shelter and escape from the elements. Blind snakes and worm snakes are good examples. Many burrowing snakes have sharp pointed snouts that are good for shoveling, or they have an enlarged scale on the nose like the Shield-nose Snake (*Aspidelaps scutatus*). Other adaptations include cylindrical bodies with highly polished scales, greatly reduced eyes, and a short tail that ends in a sharp spike. The spiky tail is used as an anchor, the snake digging it into the side of a burrow while pushing itself forward.

Aquatic Movement. Some snakes, like the sea snakes, spend virtually their entire lives in water and have laterally compressed bodies and paddle-

shaped tails. Even the broad belly scales are replaced by smaller scales, as they are no longer required. Movement is accomplished by lateral undulations in the normal serpent fashion.

Speed. Most people have heard of a snake chasing a man on horseback. This is, of course, a fallacy, as the maximum speed of a snake is grossly exaggerated. People can walk faster than most snakes can move. The maximum speed of a large, fast-moving snake such as a Black Mamba is no more than 11 to 15 km/h (7 to 9 mi/h). Snakes never chase after people, as they are shy and retiring. Snakes do strike with amazing speed and accuracy and need not do so from a coiled position, as is often thought.

A Yellow Ratsnake (Elaphe obsoleta quadrivittata) *uses its strongly keeled belly scales to climb up a palm tree.*

CLIMBING

Though many snakes climb into trees and bushes from time to time, some are especially adapted to an arboreal existence. Such snakes are either long and slim, and move about in trees effectively using lateral undulations to move horizontally, or short and stubby. Among the latter are pythons and boas and various pit vipers. They make use of a prehensile tail, which is wrapped around a branch as an anchor, in case the snake loses its grip. Tropical vipers usually have large heads, very prominent eyes, and pointed snouts. These snakes move slowly, relying heavily on excellent camouflage to remain undetected.

A further adaptation to an arboreal existence is strongly keeled scales and belly scales, known as ventral scales, that are sharply angled at the edges. The Yellow Ratsnake (*Elaphe o. quadrivittata*) has such belly scales and can easily negotiate the smooth trunk of a palm tree.

Flying Snakes. The Indo-Pacific flying snakes of the genus *Chrysopelia* are lizard eaters. They climb the smooth bark of coconut palm trees, using their strongly keeled belly scales, in search of food. When they choose to move to the next palm tree, or when threatened, they launch themselves into the air from as high as 20 m (66 ft) or even higher, expanding the rib cage to such an extent that the belly scales become concave, and make undulating movements in the air. They are said to glide across distances of 10 m (33 ft) but always descend rapidly while doing so. Despite landing heavily, they rarely injure themselves. The name "flying snake" is therefore a misnomer, as they cannot fly but rather parachute downward.

FEEDING

Snakes feed on a wide variety of prey, including small mammals, birds and their eggs, fish, amphibians, lizards, other snakes, and invertebrates, but the majority of snakes eat rodents.

Some snakes await their prey in ambush, be it on the ground or in trees. This applies to many of the pit vipers and heavy-bodied snakes, such as the Gaboon Viper (*Bitis gabonica*). Other snakes actively hunt their prey, doing so during the day or at night. A major advantage that a snake has over other predators, such as cats and hawks, is that it can enter a rodent burrow and not just catch one rodent but devour an entire rodent family in one session.

In order to locate their prey, snakes make use of various senses. It is commonly thought that snakes have poor vision, as they often appear to notice only moving prey. This may well be the case, but some of the arboreal snakes, such as the African Tree Snake (*Dispholidus typus*), have excellent vision and easily spot their prey over long distances. As snakes do not have external ear holes and cannot hear airborne sound, they cannot rely on their ability to hear to detect prey. They are sensitive to vibrations, which are picked up through the lower jaw, and can therefore sense the presence of some prey. The tongue is very important in locating prey, especially for snakes that forage among plant debris. The tongue flicks constantly, even once the prey is spotted. Pit vipers, including the rattlesnakes, and pythons and boas make use of heat detectors to locate warm-blooded prey. This method of locating prey is highly effective,

especially in pitch darkness.

Once the prey is located, snakes use several methods to secure it. The most primitive method of securing and killing prey is by constriction. The snake will latch on to its prey with its numerous sharp teeth and immediately throw a few coils around it. It then tightens its coils as its prey exhales and soon suffocates it. Small prey animals are killed quickly, but larger ones may take much longer to die. This could be dangerous to the snake, as it could be injured in the ensuing struggle.

A number of snakes grasp their prey in their powerful jaws and swallow them alive. This is more common in the primitive burrowing snakes but also occurs in larger snakes.

While many colubrid snakes have no fangs and rely largely on constriction to kill their prey, others have toxic saliva that is chewed into the prey.

The more advanced snakes make use of their fangs and venom to kill their prey. Rear-fanged snakes, like the African Tree Snake (*Dispholidus typus*), grasp their prey and hang on while their venom slowly takes effect. They often chew up and down their prey to spread their slow-acting venom. Other snakes have more effective fangs situated in the front of the mouth, coupled with venoms that are fast-acting. These snakes sometimes hang on to their prey while the venom takes effect, but many of them merely strike at their prey, inject venom, and let the prey move off and die. Thereafter the snake leisurely follows the scent of its prey, which it then inspects before eating by flicking its tongue.

An albino Corn Snake (Elaphe guttata) *kills a mouse by suffocating it and then swallows it headfirst. Snakes cannot chew their food, but are able to swallow prey much larger than their own heads.*

A Night Adder (Causus rhombeatus) *grabs a toad that looks far too big to swallow but has no problem in doing so.*

Snakes are able to consume prey much larger than their own heads. As they cannot chew, they swallow their prey whole. In most instances the snake locates the head of its prey and then slowly swallows it, drawing it into its mouth with its fangs or teeth, often pressing against the ground to assist the swallowing process. Such a meal could last a snake a week or two, depending on the size of the prey and the temperature. In winter, during cold spells, snakes go without food for six months or longer. Juvenile snakes, because they need to grow more rapidly and usually eat smaller prey, eat more often than adults. Many juveniles also feed on prey very different from that of the adults.

While many snakes are opportunistic feeders and prey on what is readily available, others are specialized feeders and are very selective when it comes to choosing food. The African egg-eaters of the genus *Dasypeltis* feed exclusively on birds' eggs and will raid nests on the ground and in trees in search of food. They also have the uncanny ability to locate birds' eggs from great distances. Once an egg is located, it is swallowed as far as the neck region. The egg is then slit, using a bony projection in the neck, its contents swallowed, and the eggshell, after being crushed into a neat little package, is regurgitated. Other snakes, like some of the cobras, also eat eggs but swallow them whole. There are many other specialized feeders, like the African Night Adder (*Causus rhombeatus*), which preys mainly on frogs and toads and is found in damp localities. Tree-living snakes, like the Emerald Tree Boa (*Corallus caninus*), are especially adapted to eating warm-blooded prey in trees. In addition to heat sensory pits, this snake has massive fanglike teeth that can securely grasp a struggling bird on which it preys. The fangs are long so that the snake can securely hang on to the bird as it struggles after it has been grabbed. Another important adaptation is the snake's prehensile tail. When it lunges out with most of its body to catch a bird, it anchors onto a branch with its tail and also hangs from its tail while constricting and swallowing its prey.

In order to trap their prey, some specialized snakes have

CANNIBALISM

A number of snakes are snake-eating, or ophiophagus. These snakes do not necessarily prey on their own species but feed on a variety of snakes, which may include their own type. They are thus not strictly cannibalistic. Some of the snake-eaters are not venomous, but their prey includes venomous species. The King Cobra (*Ophiophagus hannah*), as its scientific name implies, feeds exclusively on other snakes. Vipers are eaten carefully, as their long fangs could pierce vital organs, should the predator get bitten. The African File Snake (*Mehelya capensis*) may take the odd toad but prefers snakes. It is a harmless snake with a triangular body, hence its common name, and prowls around at night in search of other snakes. It will bite onto a snake, and a lengthy battle may follow before the prey is overcome. It is then swallowed headfirst. In many instances the prey is much larger than the snake that eats it!

Other snake-eaters include some of the American king-snakes (*Lampropeltis* sp.); many of the cobras (*Naja* sp.) also feed on snakes when the opportunity arises. There have been instances of a snake's being swallowed accidentally when two snakes attempt to swallow the same food animal.

People often wonder whether snakes can be killed by their own venom or by the venom of other snakes. A snake is not harmed by its own venom, even when it swallows a rodent that was killed by that venom. Even if another individual of the same species accidentally bit another snake during feeding, such venom would cause little or no damage. However, venom from unrelated species can prove fatal.

Top. *A Rhombic Egg-eater* (Dasypeltis scabra) *stretching its jaws over a bird's egg. Once the egg is crushed and its contents swallowed, the snake regurgitates the shell.*

Bottom. *A rare Angola Dwarf Python* (Python anchietae) *makes a meal of a lovebird.*

developed a unique way of hunting. They use their tails as lures, as a trout fisherman does with an artificial fly. The Desert Side-winder (*Bitis peringueyi*) buries itself in loose sand, leaving only its eyes and the tip of its tail exposed. When a lizard is spotted, it wriggles the tail tip to imitate an insect, and when the lizard rushes forward for a meal, it is seized and eaten. Some of the pit vipers also use their tails as lures, relying on excellent camouflage to prevent being detected. The African Vine Snake (*Thelotornis capensis*) has a bright red and black tongue, which it is thought to use as a lure. Relying on excellent camouflage, often letting as much as half of its body extend into the air, the snake is thought to flick its tongue, luring inquisitive birds closer, which are then snatched once they get close enough. The little centipede-eaters of the genus *Aparallactus* feed on venomous centipedes. After the snake grabs its prey, a formidable battle follows during which the centipede may poison its attacker. It is then often released, only to be grasped again and the battle resumed. On rare occasions the snake loses the battle and then ends up being eaten by the centipede!

Although it is the exception rather than the rule, some snakes have been known to swallow enormous prey. Large Green Anacondas (*Eunectes murinus*) quite easily swallow adult pigs, while the African Rock Python (*Python sebae*) regularly eats small antelope. The Yellow Anaconda (*Eunectes notaeus*) feeds on the Yacare caiman, while other snakes are thought to be man-eaters. Although there is little doubt that the odd person has been killed and eaten by snakes, such instances are highly exceptional. A full-grown African Rock Python (*Python sebae*), Reticulated Python (*P. reticulatus*), or Green Anaconda (*Eunectes murinus*) can easily kill and consume a child or even an adult, but this rarely happens, as snakes do not generally consider humans as prey. Most reports of people attacked by giant snakes are fabricated by people seeking publicity.

REPRODUCTION

In early spring, snakes get together to mate, the male locating the female by following a scent trail that she leaves behind. He flicks his tongue across her body, twists his tail beneath hers, and mating takes place. This may occur on the ground or, in the case of arboreal snakes, in trees, with their tails hanging down and twisting for copulation to take place. The male has two penises, known as hemipenes, and one hemipenis will be everted for copulation to take place. One section of the hemipenis will be inserted into the female and inflated. Copulation may last ten minutes, but in some instances it lasts more than two days. The average duration of a mating session is one to two hours.

A month or two later the female selects a suitable site to lay her soft, leathery eggs. She chooses a hollow tree trunk, a hole in the ground, a spot among rotting vegetation, or any other suitable, damp location. The number of eggs laid depends on the species and size of the female, and varies from two to sixty eggs or more.

The eggs require a critical amount of heat and humidity to hatch two or three months later. Each of the young within the eggs has a sharp eggtooth on the tip of the nose, which is used to slit the eggshell from the inside. Hatchlings usually resemble the adults, and those from venomous parents are venomous when they hatch.

Most females, with a few exceptions, show no interest in their eggs once they have finished laying. Pythons coil around their eggs, not just to protect them but also to help with incubation. Despite being "cold-blooded," they can increase the incubating temperature of their eggs: The female has muscular contractions or tremors that seem as though she has hiccups. The energy generated from such contractions increases the incubating temperature of the eggs by a few degrees Celsius.

People often speak of snake nests, but they do not exist, except in the case of the King Cobra of Asia. The female rakes up a few branches and pieces of plant debris, and uses it as a nest. Such females are reportedly highly aggressive and actively protect their eggs.

There are many dangers to snake eggs exposed to the elements for more than two months. During that period they could dry out or be flooded;

they could be destroyed by ants; or consumed by other snakes, monitor lizards, or a variety of other scavengers. Many of the more modern snakes retain the eggs within their bodies, and the moment the eggs are ready to hatch they deposit the eggs in what resembles live birth. Most adders and vipers give birth in this manner.

Once the young hatch, they have to move off and fend for themselves, as the parents never care for them. Hatchlings shed very soon after hatching or being born and have a stomach full of yolk on which they survive for the first few days. They instinctively hunt for food and are very vulnerable during the first few weeks of life. They are preyed upon by predatory birds, other snakes, lizards, frogs and toads, a variety of mammals, including domestic cats, and some insects. Because of the severe predation, some species, such as the Puff Adder (*Bitis arietans*), produce massive litters, exceeding one hundred young at a time.

Above. *After slitting the leathery eggshell with its egg tooth, a Brown House Snake* (Lamprophis fuliginosus) *slowly emerges from its egg.*

Opposite. *A female Burmese Python* (Python molurus bivittatus) *coils around her eggs to protect them and assist with incubation.*

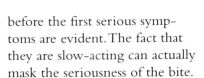

SNAKE VENOMS

Of the almost 2,400 species of snakes throughout the world, less than 10 percent possess venoms that can be considered potentially dangerous to humans. Many bites are inflicted by harmless snakes or snakes with mild venoms, often resulting in unnecessary medical procedures. The opposite also happens, and people bitten by deadly snakes receive inadequate medical care. Many of today's serious snake-bite incidents, some with fatal results, happen while people are capturing or handling snakes, at snake parks or in private collections.

If a person is bitten by a venomous snake and taken to the hospital, it is essential to identify the snake responsible for that bite. Generally speaking, however, snake venoms can be divided into three major groups.

Most of the vipers or adders, and a few cobras, have predominantly cytotoxic or cell-destroying venoms. The symptoms following a bite from one of these snakes may include pain, swelling, necrosis, weak pulse, shock, vomiting, and general weakness.

The majority of elapids, including the cobras and the mambas, have predominantly neurotoxic venoms. Such bites are usually less painful; there is little or no swelling, but drowsiness, drooping of the eyes, numbness of the lips, difficulty in swallowing and breathing, nausea, headache, and blurred vision occur. These bites may well be the most dangerous because of the fast-acting venoms that some of the elapids possess.

Some of the rear-fanged snakes, including the African Tree Snake and African Vine Snake, have very powerful hemotoxic venoms that cause massive internal bleeding. These venoms are slow-acting, sometimes taking more than a day before the first serious symptoms are evident. The fact that they are slow-acting can actually mask the seriousness of the bite.

Among the snakes that are considered extremely dangerous to humans, the African Black Mamba (*Dendroaspis polylepis*) deserves special mention. Of venomous snakes it is second in size only to the King Cobra of Asia. It is a fast and alert snake and is able to inject a massive dose of venom in a single bite. One snake possesses enough venom to kill up to half a dozen people. The Russell's Viper (*Vipera russelli*) of Asia is thought to be the species that causes the

The enormous fangs of the Puff Adder (Bitis arietans) *are connected to the venom glands at the back of the jaw via a narrow duct. When the snake applies muscular pressure on its venom glands, the venom is forced forward and passes down the center of the hollow fangs.*

most bites of any snake in the world. It is responsible for many human deaths in India, Sri Lanka, Burma, and other Asian countries every year. Like the Black Mamba, it has enough venom to kill several people.

Other medically important venomous snakes include the Indian Krait (*Bungarus caeruleus*) of India, Sri Lanka, and Bangladesh; the north African and Asian Saw-scaled Viper (*Echis carinatus*); the African Gaboon Viper (*Bitis gabonica*) and Puff Adder (*B. arietans*); and Asia's King Cobra (*Ophiophagus hannah*). The Beaked Sea Snake (*Enhydrina schistosa*), which is found from the Persian Gulf and Madagascar to New Guinea and Australia, is said to be the most venomous snake in the world.

Experts seldom agree on the figures, but it appears that between 30,000 and 50,000 people are killed by snakebites every year. The number of bites from poisonous snakes may exceed 1 million each year. The majority of deaths, perhaps more than 25,000, occur in Asia because of the large numbers of very poisonous snakes occurring in that region, coupled with dense populations of humans.

It is estimated that between 10,000 and 15,000 people die annually from snakebites in India; slightly fewer in Sri Lanka. About 2,000 deaths are recorded annually in Burma.

South America has 3,000 to 4,000 deaths annually from snakebites. Despite the presence of large numbers of venomous snakes, the importance of snakebites as a medical problem in Africa seems insignificant. Between 10 and 15 people die every year from snakebites in South Africa. Figures are similar for the United States, where about 7,000 people are treated for snakebites but no more than 15 die in a year. Australia has the greatest variety of venomous snakes in the world but seldom has more than a few fatal snakebites in a single year.

The deadly Black Mamba (Dendroaspis polylepis) *is able to inject masses of its highly toxic venom in a single bite.*

THE USE OF SNAKE VENOMS

Venoms from deadly snakes have been used throughout the ages to cure a variety of human ailments and diseases. Homeopaths in the Western world use several snake venoms in their preparations—rattlesnake venom, for example, has been used by them to treat at least fifty different ailments.

Snake venoms have been used extensively in the treatment of hemorrhagic conditions, relief of severe pain, severe nose bleeds, and bleeding after tooth extractions. The venom of the Malay Pit Viper was used in the preparation of a highly effective anticoagulant to prevent blood clots. Rattlesnake venom was used early in this century in the treatment of epilepsy.

In 1933 a New York physician named Adelph Monaelesser claimed that cobra venom could be used as an effective analgesic. It was used quite extensively for the next two decades.

Snake venoms were used for their pain-relieving properties as recently as 1940 and are today employed in research by biochemists and molecular biologists. Venoms are also being used in the preparation of products used in preservatives, meat tenderizers, fertilizers, and even cosmetics. Research into their antiviral and antibacterial properties continues.

Snake venom is used throughout the world for the production of antivenom serum (antivenin). Snake venom is collected by forcing a snake to bite through a thin layer of material placed over a glass container. The snake is grasped behind the head by a handler and its mouth placed over the container. Some handlers use mild electric shocks to stimulate the venom glands and so draw the maximum venom at each milking session. A small quantity of the venom is then injected into a horse, activating the horse's immune system. Antibodies to the venom are produced and obtained by extracting blood from the animal.

The serum, which contains the antibodies, is separated from the blood and is purified for use in humans. Such serum, or antivenin, is often lifesaving in the case of serious snakebites.

HABITAT

Except for the polar regions, a few large islands, such as Ireland and New Zealand, and several small islands in the Atlantic and Pacific Oceans, snakes are found in a variety of habitats throughout the world, on land, in freshwater, and even in the oceans. Though some snakes are found in a variety of habitats, snakes are usually divided into four categories of habitat: burrowing, terrestrial, arboreal, and aquatic.

Burrowing. Most true burrowing snakes are dark in color with cylindrical bodies, highly polished scales, indistinct heads with small eyes, and a tail frequently ending in a cone. Most typical of the burrowing snakes are members of the genera *Typhlops* and *Leptotyphlops*. They spend most of their lives in their underground burrows, where they hunt for ants and termites and their eggs. These snakes are found in damp soil on the forest floor, or in soil protected by bushes. Some of them have adapted to living in the savannas and favor deserted termite mounds, especially during winter. They seldom come to the surface, but if they do it is at night, especially after rains. Other burrowing snakes, like the Calabar Ground Python (*Calabaria reinhardti*), live in loose plant debris and are often found close to the surface. Even in drier environments such as savannas, snakes like the Stiletto Snake (*Atractaspis bibroni*) of Africa burrow into loose sand in search of food, but only close to the surface.

Terrestrial. The vast majority of snakes are mainly terrestrial, though many of them venture into shrubs and trees or even water. They are found in deserts,

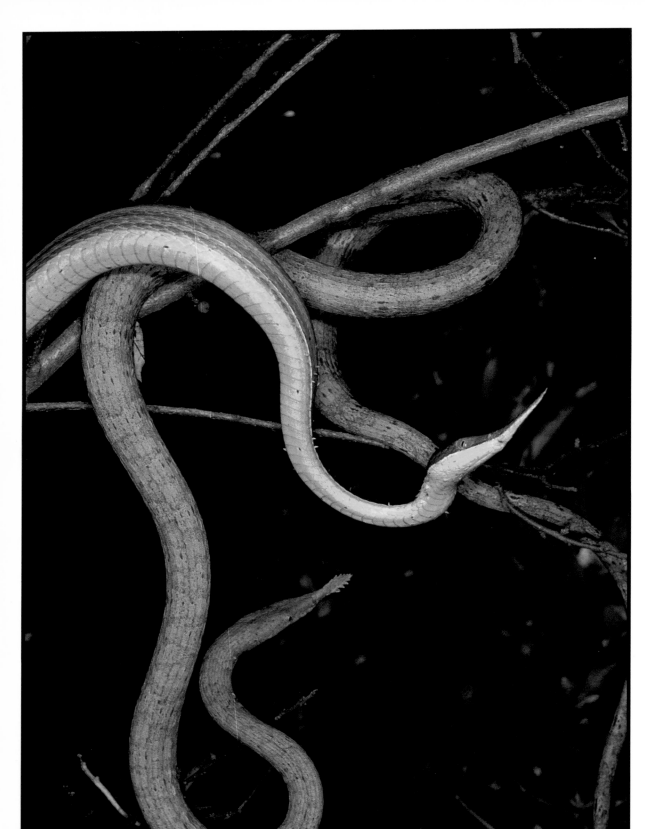

The bizarre-looking Leaf-nosed Snake (Langaha sp.) is endemic to the island of Madagascar where it feeds on frogs, lizards, and birds.

not look much different from many terrestrial snakes. The sea snakes, on the other hand, have adapted markedly to their aquatic existence, and most of them have laterally compressed bodies with paddle-shaped tails. Other adaptations include very small eyes and greatly reduced ventral scales. They also have nostrils situated high up on the head; these nostrils can seal off, preventing saltwater from entering the lungs. These snakes inhabit the intertropical coasts of the eastern Indian Ocean and the western Pacific Ocean, where most of them are found in shallow water, sometimes living on coral reefs. As they live in the warmer oceans, they do not have problems regulating their body temperature. Sea snakes prey on fish and other aquatic creatures. Some of them go onto sandy islets, especially to lay eggs, while others spend most of their lives in the water and give birth to live young. The Yellow-bellied Sea Snake (*Pelamis platurus*) is the only true pelagic, or ocean-living, sea snake and inhabits streams within the ocean.

The Elephant Trunk Snake (Acrochordus arafurae) *is strictly aquatic and appears almost helpless on land. Even its body scales are specially adapted for its aquatic existence.*

savannas, scrublands, and forests, including tropical rain forests. Some are heavy-bodied, like the African Puff Adder (*Bitis arietans*), while others, like the American racers (*Coluber* sp.), are slender and fast-moving. They spend most of their lives on the ground, where they hunt for food; otherwise, they seek refuge when they are not active.

Arboreal. Some snakes are arboreal or semiarboreal, living in shrubs and trees. They inhabit such trees and shrubs in dry savannas, coastal bush, and forests. While some snakes, like the African Vine Snake (*Thelotornis* sp.), are usually found close to the ground, others favor the tops of trees, like the Flying Snake (*Chrysopelia* sp.) of southern Asia.

Aquatic. While many snakes favor damp localities, such as the Mangrove Snake (*Boiga dendrophila*) of the Malay Peninsula and adjacent Sumatra, they cannot be considered true aquatic snakes and are referred to as semiaquatic. The water cobras of the genus *Boulengerina* from Africa and the Asian elephant trunk snakes of the genus *Acrochordus* are good examples of true aquatic snakes, the latter even having modified body scales and eyes high up on the head. Aquatic snakes inhabit a wide variety of freshwater and brackish water environments. Some of them, like the African water snakes of the genus *Lycodonomorphus*, are excellent swimmers, while others, such as the Green Anaconda (*Eunectes murinus*) and the Blood Python

(*Python curtus*), tend to move about more leisurely. While these semiaquatic snakes have adapted to their environments, more often than not they do

The deadly Cape Cobra (Naja nivea) *from South Africa inhabits a wide variety of habitats and also frequents human dwellings.*

Snake Families

Snakes have been classified into groups that share similar characteristics, but such classification is limited to the extent of our present knowledge. It must be remembered that this classification is a man-made system that is dynamic and changes continuously as our knowledge of snakes and their evolutionary relationships increase.

All snakes belong to the group or order Squamata. They are then divided further

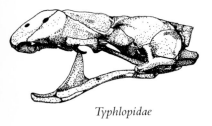

Typhlopidae

into various suborders, infra-orders, superorders, families, and subfamilies.

Among the small burrowing snakes are the families Anomo-lepididae, Typhlopidae, and

Leptotyphlopidae. The Typh-lopidae, or blind snakes, are differentiated from the other families in that they have solid teeth on the upper jaw only, whereas the Leptotyphlopidae, commonly referred to as thread or worm snakes, have solid teeth on the lower jaw only. The Anomolepididae are found in Central and South America, while the Typhlopidae and Leptotyphlopidae are found throughout most of the world.

Pythons of the family Pythonidae are found through-out Asia, Africa, and Australia. These primitive snakes, often referred to as Old World snakes, are all egg-laying.

The family Boidae includes

Pythonidae

various live-bearing boas and anacondas from the Americas, the Pacific, and Madagascar. These snakes, like the pythons, are also primitive.

Wart snakes or elephant trunk snakes of the family Acrochor-

didae are completely aquatic but share characteristics with both pythons and boas. They are found from Asia to Australia and have rasplike scales.

Most of the modern snakes throughout the world are placed in the family Colubridae. While

Colubridae

many of these snakes are harm-less, others are venomous and have grooved fangs situated quite far back in the mouth.

The family Elapidae includes mambas, cobras, and the coral snakes. They have short, fixed fangs with canals for venom injection, and the fangs are situated in the front of the mouth. This family also includes two subfamilies of sea snakes, the primitive Laticaudinae and the Hydrophiinae.

The most advanced group of

snakes are placed in the family Viperidae—snakes with large, retractable fangs and enclosed canals for venom injection. This family includes the sub-family Crotalinae, the pit vipers and rattlesnakes, and members of the subfamily Viperinae, the true vipers from Africa and Eurasia.

As mentioned, the entire system of classification is subject to review, and there is no doubt that the older classifications group together snakes that are

Viperidae

not closely related. However, there still is not sufficient information to finalize a sound system of classification.

Although many colubrid snakes have no fangs, they may have numerous large teeth like this Green Tree Python (Chondropython viridis) from Papua New Guinea.

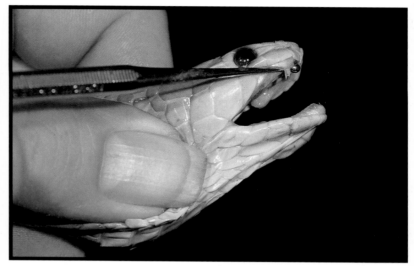

Rear-fanged snakes like the Boomslang (Dispholidus typus) have short fangs situated roughly below and behind the eyes.

The elapids, including cobras and mambas, have short, fixed fangs that are situated right in the front of the mouth.

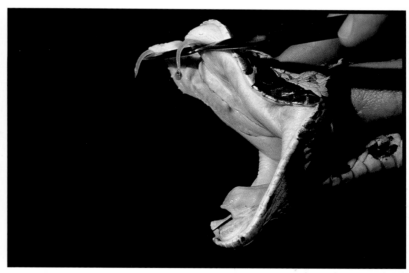

Adders and vipers have large, hinged fangs in the front of the mouth that fold back against the roof of the mouth when not in use.

Beauty Snake (Elaphe taeniura).

GALLERY OF SNAKES

THREAD SNAKES or WORM SNAKES

Leptotyphlops sp.

Thread snakes or worm snakes are usually very small and thin. Like blind snakes, they are burrowers and spend most of their lives underground. They have no teeth in the upper jaw.

There are more than seventy species of thread snakes, and they are found throughout Africa, except for the Sahara; in Amazonia and Central America; as well as in Asia, including India. They do not occur in Australasia, or eastern or southern Asia.

Thread snakes are wormlike in appearance with very thin cylindrical bodies that are usually dark in color. Most of them have blunt heads with short tails and vary in length from 8 to 30 cm (3 to 12 in). They are very primitive and their eyes are covered with scales. It is believed that thread snakes can only distinguish between light and dark. These snakes also have internal vestiges of a pelvic girdle, and some scientists believe they are related to lizards, not to snakes.

The thread snake spends virtually its entire life underground, be it in a deserted termite mound, under a rock, in rotting logs, or among the roots of grass tufts where there is an abundance of food. Females are egg-laying, producing one to seven elongated eggs that may be attached like sausages. The eggs are minute and resemble rice grains. At least one species is known to coil around its eggs to protect them.

These snakes are seldom seen but may surface in the early evenings for a short period. They may be flushed from their flooded burrows or exposed during gardening operations or when moving rocks or logs. Thread snakes are completely harmless.

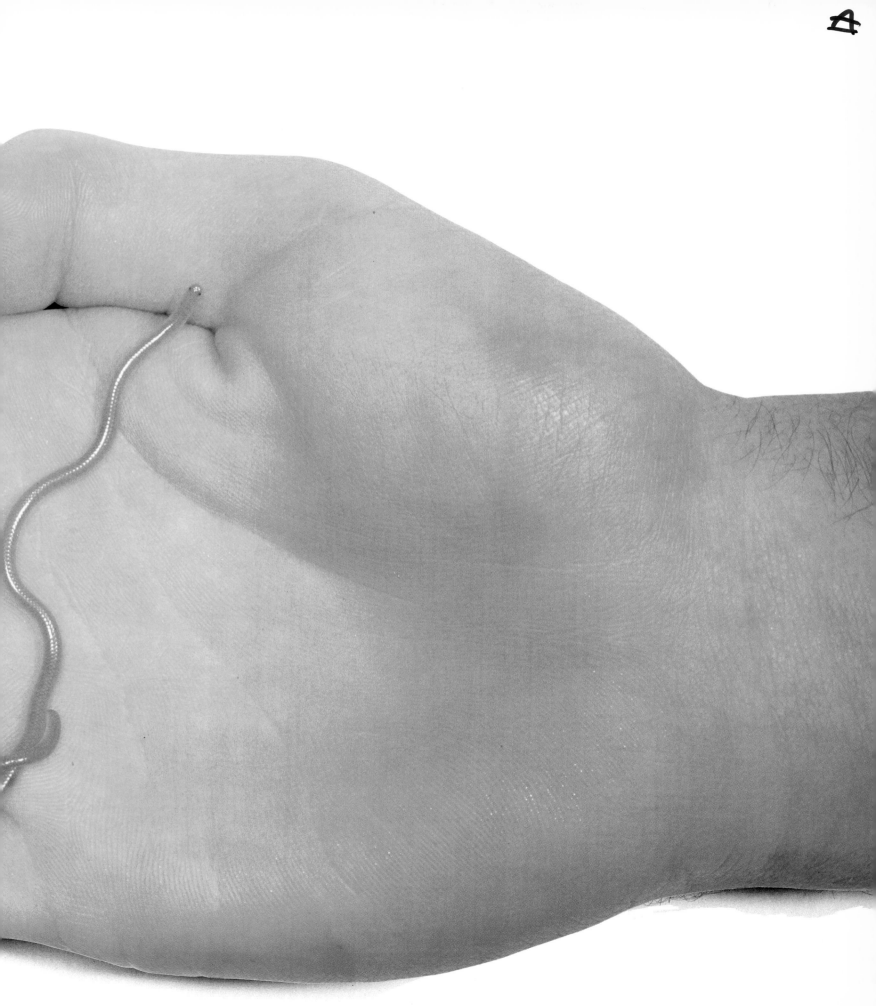

SCHLEGEL'S GIANT BLIND SNAKE
Typhlops schlegelii

Blind snakes are found throughout the tropical regions of the world and are most abundant in Africa and Asia. They are primitive snakes, lacking teeth in the lower jaw, and prey largely on termites. As they spend most of their lives in burrows underground, they have smooth cylindrical bodies with highly polished scales. Most blind snakes are quite similar in appearance and color. The head of this snake is indistinct, unlike most other snakes. As there is little use for eyes underground, the eyes are reduced and covered by enlarged scales. The tail is very short and ends with a thornlike scale. Most species of blind snakes are thought to be egg-layers.

Schlegel's Giant Blind Snake occurs in southern Africa, both in South Africa and Mozambique. It averages 60 cm (2 ft) in length but may reach a length of 95 cm (3 ft). The preferred habitats of this snake include coastal bush or savanna, where it is often found in soil under rocks or logs. Females lay from twelve to sixty eggs at a time.

GREEN ANACONDA
Eunectes murinus

The Green Anaconda is commonly referred to as one of the giant snakes. It is found in Trinidad and tropical South America east of the Andes to Bolivia and northern Paraguay in the south. There have been many reports of individuals measuring 15 m (49 ft) or even 25 m (82 ft) in length. The New York Zoological Society has offered a reward for a live specimen exceeding 30 feet (approximately 10 m) in length. Despite many expeditions to the Amazon to catch such a specimen, the reward money has never been claimed.

This snake actually averages 4 to 6 m (13 to 20 ft), exceptions reaching 8 m (26 ft) in length. The maximum length of the Green Anaconda is probably close to 10 m (33 ft), but no specimen exceeding 8.5 m (28 ft) has ever reached a zoo or snake park anywhere in the world. While the Green Anaconda is undoubtedly the largest snake in the Western Hemisphere, it vies with the Reticulated Python of Asia as the largest snake in the world. The Green Anaconda is a much bulkier snake, and one of similar length to a Reticulated Python would be much heavier. The Green Anaconda is therefore considered the heaviest snake in the world.

It is by far the most aquatic of the giant snakes, favoring swamps, shallow streams, and sluggish rivers. Though primarily active at night, it is often encountered during the day and is fond of basking. The Green Anaconda is usually found in heavily vegetated areas, where it ventures onto logs and thick branches to bask, only to escape into water if disturbed. Individuals often remain underwater with just the nose and eyes exposed. If the snake is disturbed, it pulls the head underwater as well but makes little attempt to move off. It is not aggressive and seldom attempts to bite when handled for the first time.

Like the other giant snakes, it kills its prey by suffocation. It feeds on mammals such as deer, goats, dogs, tapirs, capybara, and peccaries but may also take caimans, turtles, waterfowl, game birds, and fish. Females give birth to up to fifty or more live young at a time.

A great deal of myth surrounds the Green Anaconda, and there are numerous fallacies about it that are passed on from generation to generation. It is even said that anacondas have a preference for pregnant women, perhaps a myth that originated from jealous husbands who wanted to keep their young wives indoors.

YELLOW ANACONDA
Eunectes notaeus

The Yellow Anaconda has black or brown blotches, saddles, and streaks against a yellow to greenish yellow or golden tan background, which distinguishes this snake from the rather dull-colored Green Anaconda. It inhabits swamps, marshes, and vegetated banks of sluggish rivers and streams in southern Brazil, Bolivia, Paraguay, and northern Argentina. It is much smaller than the Green Anaconda, averaging 3 m (10 ft) in length with a maximum length of 4.6 m (15 ft). Like its larger relative, the Yellow Anaconda is highly aquatic, and an individual basking on the shore will quickly slither into water when disturbed, where it may hide on the muddy bottom.

Once it feels safe, it will return to the surface, carefully exposing the top of its head to the level of its eyes. The Yellow Anaconda preys on mammals such as paca, agouti, other rodents, birds, and reptiles. Juveniles reportedly also feed on fish. Individuals will invariably concentrate on prey species that are abundant in their immediate environment. It also preys on the yacare caiman. The caiman is seized at the base of the head, preventing it from using its powerful jaws in retaliation. Several coils are

quickly thrown around the crocodilian and it is suffocated. Thereafter it is swallowed headfirst. Although this snake has no venom, it does have many strongly recurved needle-sharp teeth and is capable of inflicting a nasty bite.

EMERALD TREE BOA
Corallus caninus

This beautifully colored constrictor lives in trees and bushes in rain forests, usually next to sluggish rivers or in swamps and marshes. The Emerald Tree Boa is found in the Amazon basin from Peru and Bolivia through Brazil to the Guianas. It spends virtually its entire life in trees, where it sleeps during the day, draped over a branch, and is extremely difficult to see because of its excellent camouflage. At night it hunts for food, making use of its highly effective thermal receptors to locate warm-blooded prey. Birds and small mammals, including bats, make up part of its diet. This snake has massive fanglike teeth that enable it to capture and hold on to birds with ease. The prey is seized, suffocated, and swallowed headfirst while the snake is suspended upside down from a branch, often hanging on with its prehensile tail. Adults average 2.2 m (7 ft) in length.

ARGENTINE BOA

Boa constrictor occidentalis

This is the southernmost race of boa constrictor and is found in Paraguay and Argentina. It is active at night and spends its days in an animal burrow, hollow log, or similar shelter. It may venture into trees but is more at home on the ground, where it feeds on small mammals, birds, and lizards. The young tend to spend more time in shrubs and bushes, where they forage for food. This snake has adapted to living around villages, where there is plentiful food in the form of rats and chickens. Many individuals are accidentally shipped all over the world as stowaways among bananas and other fruit. Females give birth to between fifteen and forty live young. Like many other snakes, the Argentine Boa is an excellent swimmer. Color variation is common in snakes, and this species is no exception. There are many fallacies about this snake; some people even believe that a dog gives birth to the young and that the little snakes bark!

BOA CONSTRICTOR
Boa constrictor

Despite popular belief, the Boa Constrictor is not a dangerous inhabitant of the jungles as often portrayed in literature and films. It is found in a variety of habitats, including savanna grassland. The Peruvian variety, for example, occurs in the arid rocky plains of Peru. Boa Constrictors are common throughout the neotropics, from Mexico in the north to Argentina in the south. Though some specimens reach 5 m (16 ft) in length, this snake averages about 2.5 m (8 ft) and is not the fearsome serpent that people often imagine. It is, in fact, an inoffensive snake and poses little threat to humans. Boa Constrictors are popular in the pet trade, and thousands are bred for this purpose; many more are exported from the wild every year. These snakes may end up in private collections in the United States and throughout Europe and the Far East.

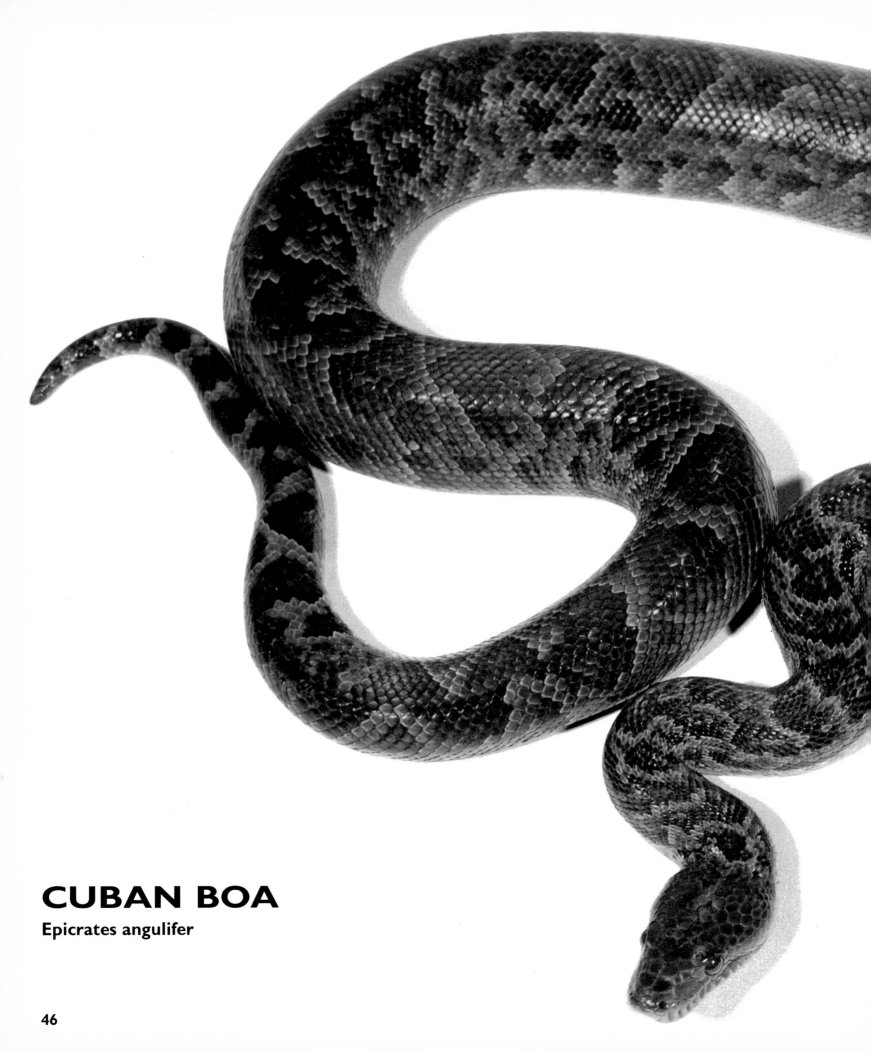

CUBAN BOA

Epicrates angulifer

This snake is found in Cuba, the Isle of Pines, and Cayo Cantiles, and is the largest of this group of snakes, occurring throughout the Caribbean islands. Specimens up to 4.5 m (15 ft) in length have been recorded, but such large snakes are rare nowadays. The Cuban Boa is a ground dweller but may venture into trees and shrubs. At night it seeks shelter in holes in the ground and sometimes in rock piles. Hunting for food takes place in the day but may extend into dusk during summer when it is still warm. Food includes small mammals, especially rodents such as hutia, and birds. Caves are frequented in search of bats. The Cuban Boa inhabits wooded, grassy plains. Unfortunately, most of its habitat was destroyed at the beginning of this century as sugar cane farming became popular. Local people, on seeing a snake, are quick to grab a machete and kill it. To worsen matters, this snake frequents human dwellings in search of rats. As the number of Cuban Boas in the wild dwindles, campaigns have been initiated to educate local people about snakes. This species appears on a Cuban postage stamp.

MADAGASCAN GROUND BOA
Acrantophis madagascariensis

Also known as the Malagasy Ground Boa, this snake is found only in Madagascar, where it inhabits sparse open woodland and dry forest regions. It is very similar in appearance and habits to the Boa Constrictor of Central and South America. It is active at night and begins to move about from dusk onward. Days are spent hiding in mammal burrows, in fallen logs, or in piles of debris. Food consists of small mammals and birds and, like other boas, the snake constricts its prey prior to swallowing it. Unlike the adults, the young often venture onto shrubs and bushes in search of food. The Madagascan Ground Boa hibernates during the colder months, from May to July. Females are live-bearers, producing four to six young at a time.

Like many snakes elsewhere in the world, this snake is threatened by deforestation. It is estimated that less than 10 percent of Madagascar's forests remain undisturbed. As human populations expand, so do their destructive slash-and-burn agricultural practices. Fortunately, the Madagascan Ground Boa adapts well to areas that have been disturbed. However, a further threat comes from the local skin trade: Snakes are killed and their skins turned into wallets and belts. These products are sold locally to tourists. This snake has been considered endangered since 1977. It has become highly sought after in private collections, and enthusiasts may pay over U.S. $5,000 for a newborn individual.

AFRICAN
ROCK PYTHON

Python sebae

The African Rock Python
inhabits open savanna,
where it prefers rocky areas and
riverine scrub. It is found
throughout sub-Saharan Africa
but is absent from deserts and
rain forests. It is very fond of
basking, especially after feeding,
but is more active at night,
when it locates its warm-
blooded prey by means of heat
receptors situated in sensory pits
on the upper lip. Its diet consists
of hares, cane rats, monkeys,
small antelope, and game birds.
Though not poisonous, this
python has numerous sharp,
recurved teeth and is capable of
inflicting a painful wound. A
large female, which may mea-
sure more than 4 m (13 ft) in
length, usually lays thirty
to fifty eggs but can lay as
many as one hundred
eggs. She will coil
around her eggs
throughout
incubation to
protect them
and assist
with incu-
bation.
The young,
each measur-
ing about
60 cm (2 ft),
move off after
hatching and
have to fend
for themselves.

RETICULATED PYTHON
Python reticulatus

The Reticulated Python is found in rain forests, woodland, and adjacent grassland in Southeast Asia and the nearby Pacific islands, where it frequents rivers and streams. It is one of the two largest snakes in the world, the other being the Green Anaconda. Although the average length of this snake is about 4 to 6 m (13 to 20 ft), individuals exceeding 10 m (33 ft) have been reported. Specimens exceeding 7.5 m (25 ft) are to be seen in some zoos and snake parks. The Reticulated Python feeds on mammals, birds, and large lizards, such as the monitor lizard. A large individual could quite easily swallow an adult pig. There have been many reports over the years, most of them unsubstantiated, of Reticulated Pythons' killing and eating people, and some photographs have appeared to prove such cases. There is little doubt that people have been eaten by this snake, but such instances are rare. Females produce about fifty eggs but may lay as many as one hundred at a time. Like most pythons, the female coils around her eggs during incubation and will not hesitate to bite if disturbed.

ROYAL PYTHON
Python regius

 The Royal Python, with its head on the right side of the photograph, is native to central and west Africa, where it favors savanna and sparsely wooded plains. During the day it sleeps in mammal burrows or similar underground retreats, and at night it hunts for small mammals. It is the smallest of the African pythons, averaging about 1 m (3 ft) in length. It is also known as the Ball Python for its habit of coiling into a tight ball when threatened, carefully concealing its head between coils. Females lay about six or seven eggs and coil around their eggs during incubation, which lasts about three months. The Royal Python is very popular in the pet trade, and thousands are shipped to pet dealers in Europe and the United States every year. This snake is also a delicacy among various tribal groups, and many snakes are slaughtered for their skins. The Royal Python is now considered a threatened species throughout most of its range.

The Angolan Dwarf Python inhabits dry rocky sandy plains regions and riverine bush in Angola and northern Namibia. It is a rare and elusive snake that is active at night and is seldom encountered. Like the Royal Python, it feeds on small mammals such as gerbils and rats, though ground birds are also taken. This snake is similar in size to the Royal Python and is

also known to coil up into a tight ball when threatened. About five eggs are laid once a year. Because it is extremely rare and seldom encountered, the Angolan Dwarf Python is highly sought after in the pet trade, even though it is protected and may not be collected.

ROYAL PYTHON with ANGOLAN DWARF PYTHON

Python regius and P. anchietae

BLOOD PYTHON

Python curtus

This short, stubby python occurs in Malaysia, Sumatra, and Borneo, where it prefers highly aquatic environments such as swamps, marshes, and streams in rain forests. Though not poisonous, it is quite aggressive and quick to strike.

Adults may exceed 2 m (7 ft) in length but are usually much smaller. The color varies from bright orange to yellow or blood red, hence the common name. Food consists of small mammals and birds, which are seized, constricted, and then swallowed headfirst. Females produce six to twelve eggs and, like most pythons, coil around their eggs throughout incuba-tion. By coiling around the eggs, the female protects them from predators and also assists with incubation through thermoregulation. While coiled around her eggs, she will twitch her body muscles to generate heat, increasing the incubation temperature by as much as 5°C (41°F). During incubation the female will refrain from eating but may leave her eggs to drink water. Males do not assist in the incubation process. Once the eggs hatch, the young move off on their own and are not protected by the parents. Most pythons have little "spurs" at the base of the tail. These are vestigial hind limbs and, other than supposedly functioning to some degree in courtship, serve no known purpose. The Blood Python is sought after by private collectors, and thousands are collected and exported for the pet trade every year.

This attractive snake occurs over much of Australia, except the central and western regions, and in New Guinea. It is found in a wide variety of habitats, from rain forests to deserts. In some areas it is largely tree-living, while in other areas it inhabits burrows made by other animals. Carpet Pythons are most active at night, when they hunt their warm-blooded prey using their well-developed heat sensory pits on the upper lip. Birds and mammals, including the foul-smelling possum, are preyed upon. The female deposits up to eighteen eggs in a suitable site and coils around her eggs to assist with incubation and to protect them.

CARPET PYTHON
Morelia spilotes variegata

CALABAR PYTHON

Calabaria reinhardti

The Calabar Python, also known as the Burrowing Python, is found in western Africa from Liberia eastward through the rain forest areas of the Ivory Coast, Ghana, and Nigeria. It tunnels its way through loose soil and forest floor debris, seldom exposing itself on the surface. It may also enter rodent burrows in search of food. This cylindrical, stump-tailed constrictor seldom exceeds 1 m (3 ft) in length. Its head and tail are very similar in appearance, except of course for the eyes, which are barely visible. When threatened, it presses its head into the ground, often covering it with a coil, and then elevates its tail, which it moves to and fro. If this does not have the desired effect, it coils into a tight ball, like the Royal Python, with its head concealed among the coils. Once coiled into a ball, it waits patiently for the disturbance to move off and eventually uncoils slowly when it feels safe. Local people believe that this snake has two heads and fear it. It is a harmless constrictor that seldom attempts to bite, even when handled. Females lay two to four large eggs.

EUROPEAN GRASS SNAKE
Natrix natrix

The European Grass Snake has a wide distribution covering Europe, northern Africa, and western Asia. This harmless snake is somewhat aquatic, preferring sunny spots in well-vegetated areas. Damp meadows, marshes, ditches, ponds, and rivers are frequented, where a disturbed individual will dive into water and seek shelter. Grass snakes are exceptional swimmers and are also at home in low shrubs, where they bask or hunt for food. When swimming they keep their head and neck raised above the water. Food consists of frogs, small fish, newts, salamanders, and toads. While some grass snakes prey heavily on toads, others avoid them. Hunting may take place underwater, with large prey dragged onto land before being swallowed. In most instances, the prey is still alive when swallowed. Grass snakes hibernate in winter. Females lay about thirty eggs per clutch, but young females may lay only eight to ten eggs per clutch. This snake often makes use of communal nesting areas, and as many as 1,500 eggs could be found in a suitable laying site. The European Grass Snake is preyed upon by hedgehogs, badgers, stoats, predatory birds, and even domestic poultry.

DICE SNAKE

Natrix tessellata

The harmless Dice Snake is found throughout northern and central Europe, northwestern Africa, and western Asia. It is a great deal more aquatic than the European Grass Snake and spends most of its time in and around water. It prefers clear rivers, streams, lakes, and ponds and tends to avoid muddy water. On sunny days it may bask on branches overhanging water, and several snakes may congregate to enjoy the sun. If disturbed, they quickly drop into the water. An excellent swimmer, the Dice Snake swims with its head kept above water. It is active during the day, when it will hunt for small fish and amphibians, such as newts and frogs. Fish are usually hunted while the snake is fully submerged. This snake hibernates in rock crevices or holes in the ground. Females lay six to twenty-four eggs. The Dice Snake is not often encountered, as it seldom strays far from water and quickly dives when disturbed. It is known to feign death when threatened. Captured individuals thrash about violently but seldom attempt to bite, even when handled for the first time.

Because of the shape of its head and its body markings, the Viperine Snake (described on right) may be confused with the poisonous European Adder, hence its common name. The resemblance can be seen in these photographs. As the two snakes commonly occur in the same area, the Viperine Snake is often wrongly identified as an adder and unnecessarily killed.

EUROPEAN ADDER
Vipera berus

VIPERINE SNAKE
Natrix maura

The Viperine Snake often has a zigzag pattern down its back and may resemble an adder, hence the common name. Unfortunately, this harmless snake is often mistaken for an adder and needlessly killed. It is found throughout central and southern France, northern Italy, Sardinia, Spain, the Balearic Islands, and Portugal, and in Morocco, northern Algeria, Tunisia, western Libya, and Turkey. It is fairly aquatic, preferring swamps, marshes, lakes, and streams, but is also found in fields away from water.

The Viperine Snake is very alert, both on land and in water. It is fond of basking, and many snakes may be found in one location, enjoying the morning sun. When it gets too hot, it retreats beneath rocks or moss or seeks refuge in water, where it may be seen swimming leisurely among plants. It is an excellent swimmer and may do so with its head raised above the water, otherwise it swims underwater. In shallow water it will push itself up to the surface on its tail, allowing its nostrils and eyes to protrude, before silently disappearing below the surface again. It preys on fish, eels, and amphibians. Mammals and birds may also be taken. Food may be swallowed in water, but larger prey is dragged to land and swallowed there. Females, measuring about 80 cm (3 ft), produce four to twenty eggs and lay them close to water. The Viperine Snake may hibernate for a short period south of its range. Communal hibernating takes place in the north, often with other species of snake. Rocky cavities or holes in the ground are used for this purpose.

TRANS PECOS RATSNAKE

Bogertophis subocularis

This harmless constrictor, with its unusually large eyes, occurs from west-central Mexico through southwestern Texas into south-central New Mexico. It is a desert species, preferring rocky areas with sufficient crevices. During the day it hides under rocks or down armadillo, gopher, and rodent holes, emerging at dusk when it is warm. It hunts for small mammals and birds. Juveniles also eat lizards. Adults average 80 to 120 cm (3 to 4 ft) in length, with a maximum length of 1.65 m (5 ft). Females produce an average of five eggs, with a range of three to eight. The Trans Pecos Ratsnake spends much of its time hidden among broken limestone that often lies scattered beneath much of the desert floor, seldom encountering predators and making little effort to escape if it does.

GRAY RATSNAKE
Elaphe obsoleta spiloides

The Gray Ratsnake is found from southern Illinois and adjacent Indiana south to Mississippi, western Georgia, and the Florida Panhandle. It inhabits wooded areas around swamps as well as sparse woodland in sandy soil. It is a powerful constrictor that will coil and strike repeatedly when alarmed, but the bite is harmless. The Gray Ratsnake averages 1.5 m (5 ft) in length but may exceed 2 m (7 ft). It is an excellent climber, and in parts of its distribution it frequents oak trees. It is also called the Oak Snake. Like some of the other ratsnakes, it frequents old buildings, barns, and similar derelict structures, often in suburbs and even in towns. It feeds on rodents as well as birds and their eggs. Females lay five to thirty eggs in leaf litter or under rocks. Different populations of Gray Ratsnakes vary in color. Some populations consist of snakes that are dark gray with brownish gray blotches, while other populations are smoky-white to gray with gray blotches.

YELLOW RATSNAKE

Elaphe obsoleta quadrivittata

The Yellow Ratsnake is found from central Florida north through Georgia and South Carolina to the south-eastern coastal areas of North Carolina. It favors wooded thickets, swamps, old buildings, and barns, where one may find

several shed skins draped about like props in a horror movie. It is an excellent climber and often climbs into trees, including palm trees, prior to shedding. It will remain there and only come down once it has shed its skin. It is a powerful, harmless constrictor and feeds on rodents, birds, and their eggs. Birds' nests are often raided, as are chicken coops, in search of eggs and chicks. This habit has earned it the name Chicken Snake. If threatened, it will coil the forepart of the body into an S shape, open its mouth, and hiss violently while vibrating the tail to mimic a rattlesnake. It strikes out readily.

CORN SNAKE
Elaphe guttata guttata

The Corn Snake, also known as the Red Ratsnake, is found in pine barrens from southern New Jersey, south through peninsular Florida, and west into Louisiana. It frequents sandy pine woods, sandy scrub oak, and cutover woodland. It may be found in virtually any other suitable habitat. It is mainly a terrestrial snake and is most active at night, when it forages around uprooted trees, rotten logs, log piles, and along rodent burrows in search of food. It feeds on small rodents, birds, bats, and lizards. Like some of the other ratsnakes, it may also be found in abandoned buildings and barns. It is smaller than some of its relatives, averaging just over 1 m (3 ft), with a maximum length of 1.8 m (6 ft).

Females produce nine to thirty eggs at a time. Like the Yellow Ratsnake, it will form an S shape with the anterior third of its body when threatened, rattle its tail vigorously, and strike out menacingly. Despite this formidable show, the Corn Snake is quite harmless.

BEAUTY SNAKE

Elaphe taeniura

Though quite common in zoos and snake parks, the Beauty Snake is not that common in nature. It is widely distributed throughout southern China, Burma, Laos, parts of Thailand, and Assam. The Beauty Snake inhabits a wide range of habitats, where it feeds on small mammals, including bats, and birds. It is a powerful yet harmless and inoffensive constrictor that is at home both in trees and on the ground. Many of these attractive snakes are captured and exported for the pet trade.

RUSSIAN RATSNAKE

Elaphe schrencki

This snake is found from northeast China through Korea to the eastern parts of the former Soviet Union. It is a powerful, sturdy constrictor and is not poisonous. The Russian Ratsnake inhabits wooded valleys, plains, and open montane forests in temperate regions. It actively hunts for food, and its diet includes small mammals, especially rodents, and birds and their eggs. Because of its preference for rodents, it is often found in agricultural areas. Hatchlings feed on newborn rodents. Adults average just over 1 m (3 ft) but may reach a length of 2 m (7 ft).

PAKISTAN RATSNAKE

Spalerosophis diadema

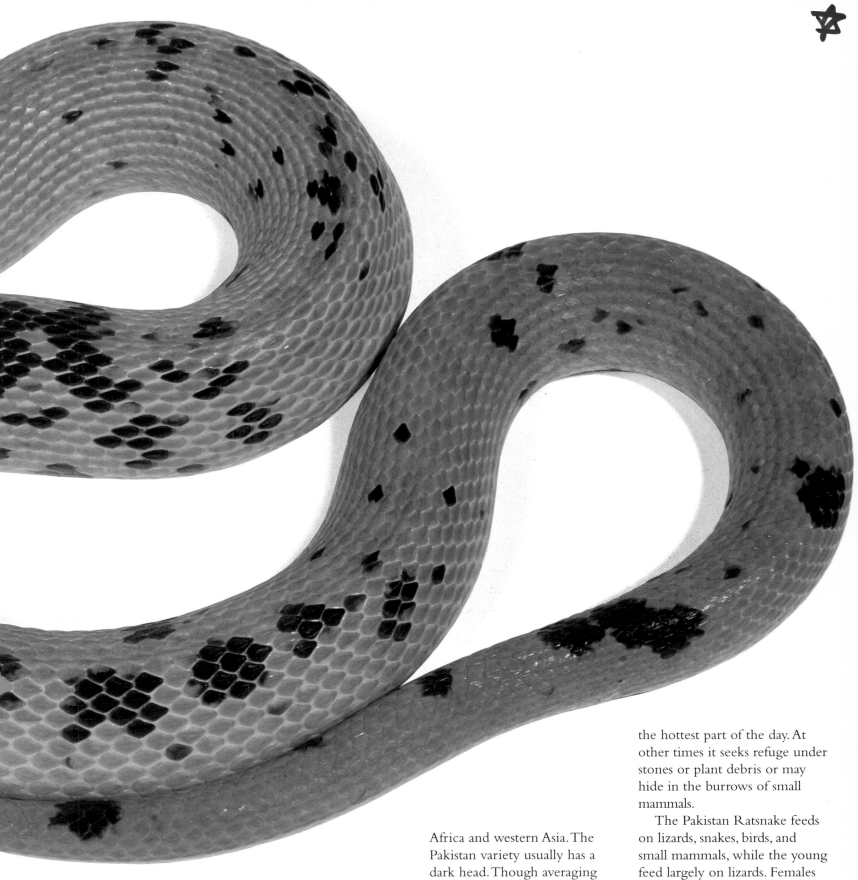

🐍 Also known as the Diadem
Snake in some parts of its
range, this snake has a wide
range over much of northern

Africa and western Asia. The
Pakistan variety usually has a
dark head. Though averaging
just over 1 m (3 ft), this powerful constrictor may exceed 2 m
(7 ft) in length. It inhabits dry
rocky plains and hillsides, where
it may be seen foraging during

the hottest part of the day. At
other times it seeks refuge under
stones or plant debris or may
hide in the burrows of small
mammals.

The Pakistan Ratsnake feeds
on lizards, snakes, birds, and
small mammals, while the young
feed largely on lizards. Females
produce twelve or more eggs,
depositing them under stones or
in burrows in the ground. Although this snake bites readily, it
is harmless.

NORTHERN PINE SNAKE

Pituophis melanoleucus

This attractive snake is found from southern New Jersey south into Virginia, Kentucky, Tennessee, and northern Alabama. It inhabits sandy pine woods, foothills, and sandhills, where it is mainly active during the day. It may forage at night during hot weather. The Northern Pine Snake is a secretive, burrowing snake that digs its own burrows or uses those of other animals. It feeds on rodents, other small mammals, and birds, which are seized and constricted. Rodents are hunted in their network of burrows, and an entire rodent family may be eaten during a single feeding session. While swallowing one rodent, the snake will immobilize the remaining rodents by pinning them against the sides of the burrow with its coils. Juvenile Pine Snakes also eat lizards. When at rest this snake seeks shelter in mammal or tortoise burrows, or under large rocks and logs. Females usually produce about eight eggs but may lay more. When threatened, it puts up quite a show by inflating its body and coiling into a striking position, with its head flattened, while hissing loudly. The tail is vibrated to mimic the poisonous rattlesnake, and the mouth may be agape. At this stage the snake will not hesitate to strike, even though it is harmless.

Campbell's Milksnake
(Lampropeltis triangulum campbelli)

Venezuela in South America. These colorful snakes are powerful but harmless constrictors that feed on a variety of vertebrates, including rodents, lizards, birds, and snakes. Even venomous snakes are eaten. They inhabit a wide variety of habitats, from deserts to forests and marshland, and occur from sea

The beautifully colored kingsnakes and milksnakes may be confused with the poisonous coral snakes. Mimicry is quite common in snakes, and there is no doubt that, to some extent, the kingsnakes and milksnakes mimic venomous snakes. Both groups, kingsnakes and milksnakes on the one hand and coral snakes on the other, commonly have red, black, and yellow bands. Not only are coral snakes often found in the same areas as milksnakes and king-snakes, but they may even be found under the same log! In most cases, coral snakes have red bands touching yellow bands, whereas milksnakes have red bands often touching black bands.

There are at least eight species and several subspecies of kingsnake and milksnake occurring from southern Ontario and southwest Quebec west to Washington, then south through the United States to Colombia, Ecuador, and

Right. *Sinaloan Milksnake*
(Lampropeltis triangulum sinaloae)

Left. *Arizona Mountain Kingsnake*
(Lampropeltis pyromelana pyromelana)

Below. *Pueblan Milksnake*
(Lampropeltis triangulum campbelli)

KINGSNAKES and MILKSNAKES
Lampropeltis sp.

Below: *California Kingsnake*
(Lampropeltis getula californiae)

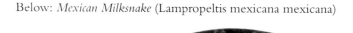
Below: *Mexican Milksnake* (Lampropeltis mexicana mexicana)

level to altitudes exceeding 3,000 m (9,843 ft) in the Andes in South America. Kingsnakes and milksnakes vary in size from 35 cm (1 ft) to nearly 2 m (7 ft). They are largely nocturnal, though individuals are known to hunt for food during the day. Females commonly lay from five to fifteen eggs. Because of the beautiful markings of these placid snakes, they have become very popular as pets throughout the world.

Above Right. *San Diego Mountain Kingsnake*
(Lampropeltis zonata pulchea)

The Honduran Milksnake occurs on the Caribbean slope of Honduras, through Nicaragua, and into northeastern Costa Rica. It is a shy, secretive snake that is active at night. At other times it seeks shelter under stones, logs, or in piles of debris. Like many other kingsnakes and milksnakes, there are many different color varieties. The name "milksnake" comes from the incorrect belief that this snake sucks milk from cows. Milksnakes often frequent barns in search of rodents but certainly do not suckle from cows! This fallacy is, however, widespread in many countries. The Honduran Milksnake feeds on small mammals, especially rodents, and birds, lizards, and snakes, including venomous types. Females are egg-laying, producing three to eighteen eggs at a time. This is one of the larger milksnakes, reaching and sometimes even exceeding 1.2 m (4 ft) in length.

BOOMSLANG
Dispholidus typus

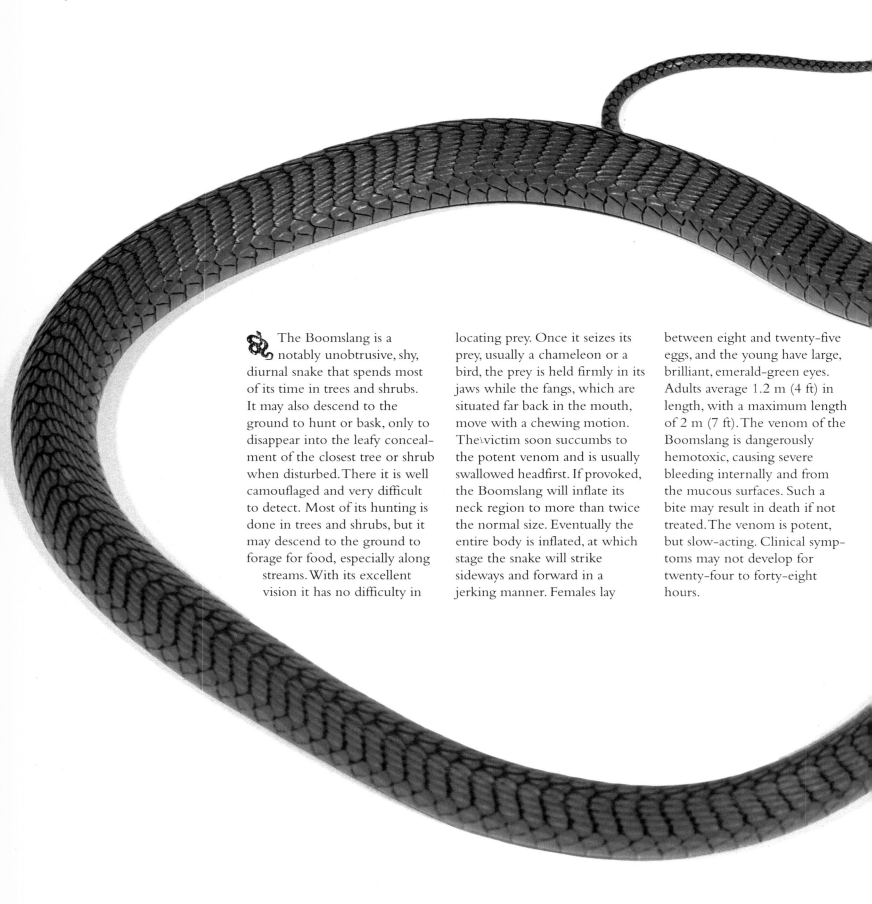

The Boomslang is a notably unobtrusive, shy, diurnal snake that spends most of its time in trees and shrubs. It may also descend to the ground to hunt or bask, only to disappear into the leafy conceal-ment of the closest tree or shrub when disturbed. There it is well camouflaged and very difficult to detect. Most of its hunting is done in trees and shrubs, but it may descend to the ground to forage for food, especially along streams. With its excellent vision it has no difficulty in locating prey. Once it seizes its prey, usually a chameleon or a bird, the prey is held firmly in its jaws while the fangs, which are situated far back in the mouth, move with a chewing motion. The victim soon succumbs to the potent venom and is usually swallowed headfirst. If provoked, the Boomslang will inflate its neck region to more than twice the normal size. Eventually the entire body is inflated, at which stage the snake will strike sideways and forward in a jerking manner. Females lay between eight and twenty-five eggs, and the young have large, brilliant, emerald-green eyes. Adults average 1.2 m (4 ft) in length, with a maximum length of 2 m (7 ft). The venom of the Boomslang is dangerously hemotoxic, causing severe bleeding internally and from the mucous surfaces. Such a bite may result in death if not treated. The venom is potent, but slow-acting. Clinical symp-toms may not develop for twenty-four to forty-eight hours.

FALSE WATER COBRA

Hydrodynastes gigas

This is a large, powerful snake that is found from eastern Bolivia, Paraguay, and southern Brazil to northern

Argentina. It is a diurnal snake that favors well-watered open scrub and cactus woodland, plantations, and even developed areas. This snake, also called the Brazilian Smooth Snake, is highly aquatic over much of its range and actively forages for food. It preys on a large variety of animals, such as fish, frogs, and toads. In drier regions it also

takes small mammals and birds. It is a rear-fanged and venomous snake, but its venom has little effect on humans. The prey is usually seized in the snake's powerful jaws and may be swallowed while still alive, despite having been envenomated. It is a large, heavy-bodied snake that often exceeds 2 m (7 ft) in length. Females lay as many as forty-two eggs at a

time. The common name is somewhat misleading, as this snake barely resembles a cobra. When threatened, it raises the forepart of its body off the ground while flattening its neck, hissing aggressively at the same time. Once threatened, it will not hesitate to bite.

GREEN VINE SNAKE

Oxybelis fulgidus

The Green Vine Snake is found in tropical rain forests, secondary forests, and thick brushland from Mexico to northern South America. In recent years it has entered human settlements and may be found in suburban hedges. With its long head, pointed snout, and very slender body and tail, it certainly resembles a vine. At times it will extend the forepart of its body horizontally or vertically into the air and freeze until an unsuspecting lizard approaches close enough to be seized. The Green Vine Snake is active during the day and spends its time climbing through trees, bushes, and tangled vines in search of food. It is extremely well camouflaged and easily mistaken for a vine. The rear-fanged Green Vine Snake preys largely on lizards, especially anoles, but birds are also taken. Once the prey is seized and envenomated, it quickly succumbs to the effect of the venom. This snake may reach 1.3 m (4 ft) in length with a maximum length of 1.6 m (5 ft). Females are egg-laying, producing four to six eggs at a time.

MADAGASCAN HOG-NOSE SNAKE
Leioheterodon modestus

This snake is native to Madagascar and inhabits a variety of habitats, from tropical rain forests through forest edges, savannas, and plains. It is a ground dweller that spends most of the day hiding in self-dug burrows, rock crevices, or beneath logs and debris. At dusk the Madagascan Hog-nose Snake forages for food such as rodents, other small mammals, and amphibians. Hatchlings feed mainly on frogs. When molested, this robust snake flattens its neck and may hiss loudly but seldom attempts to bite. It is an egg-laying species, and females produce up to twelve eggs at a time.

BIRD SNAKE
Thelotornis capensis

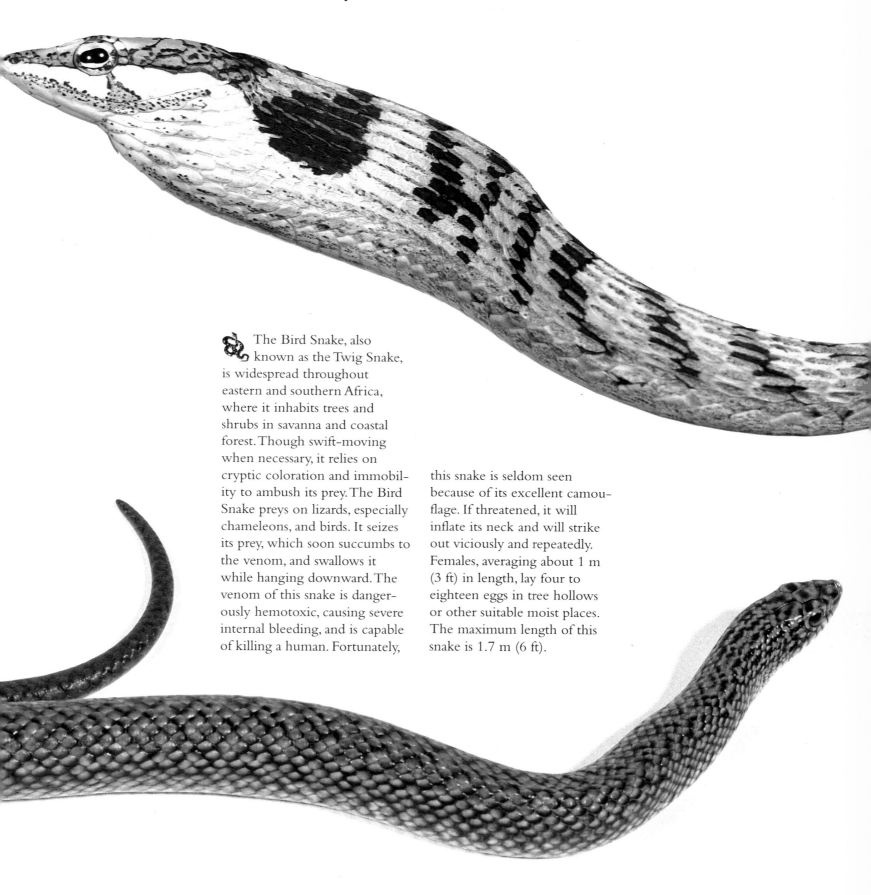

The Bird Snake, also known as the Twig Snake, is widespread throughout eastern and southern Africa, where it inhabits trees and shrubs in savanna and coastal forest. Though swift-moving when necessary, it relies on cryptic coloration and immobility to ambush its prey. The Bird Snake preys on lizards, especially chameleons, and birds. It seizes its prey, which soon succumbs to the venom, and swallows it while hanging downward. The venom of this snake is dangerously hemotoxic, causing severe internal bleeding, and is capable of killing a human. Fortunately, this snake is seldom seen because of its excellent camouflage. If threatened, it will inflate its neck and will strike out viciously and repeatedly. Females, averaging about 1 m (3 ft) in length, lay four to eighteen eggs in tree hollows or other suitable moist places. The maximum length of this snake is 1.7 m (6 ft).

RED-TAILED RATSNAKE

Gonyosoma oxycephala

This bright green snake with reddish brown tail is found in rain forests and tropical monsoon forests throughout southeastern Asia and the Philippines. It is a slender, strong snake that spends most of its time in trees, favoring green plants where it is well camouflaged. The Red-tailed Ratsnake is active during the day, when it hunts for food in mangrove forests, bamboo forests, and lowlands. It feeds on frogs, lizards, small mammals, birds, eggs, and nestling birds. Adults average 1.6 m (5 ft) but may reach a length of well over 2 m (7 ft). Females are egg-laying, producing five to twelve eggs. This snake is quite aggressive and quick to bite but is harmless.

KING COBRA

Ophiophagus hannah

The King Cobra is by far the largest and most impressive venomous snake in the world. It is found from India through Indo-China and South China to the Indo-Australian archipelago, Bali, and the Philippines. It is an inhabitant of tropical and montane woodland, where it is found near streams, in bamboo thickets, forests, mangroves, and even agricultural areas. It is active during the day, when it hunts for food, sometimes even climbing into trees and shrubs. It is at home in water and is an excellent swimmer. The King Cobra feeds on snakes, especially cobras and kraits, but also on vipers. It has to be very careful when eating the latter, as vipers have large fangs that can pierce a vital organ. This snake cannot spit its venom. Despite its reputation, it is quite timid and prefers to go into hiding when disturbed, if it has the choice. If cornered it will rear up in typical cobra fashion and may rush forward to strike with amazing accuracy. It is an extremely dangerous snake when threatened and possesses large quantities of potent venom. Surprisingly, it seldom features in snakebite incidents. It reputedly has the ability to kill an elephant with a single bite! The King Cobra has become quite rare, because of habitat destruction but also because of its size: It is difficult for such a large snake, occasionally exceeding 5 m (16 ft), to remain undetected.

This is the only snake in the world that constructs a crude nest in which it lays eggs. The

female uses loops of her body to scrape together rotting leaves and other plant debris, forming a rather crude nest. She then deposits about forty to fifty eggs and remains there throughout incubation to protect them. Some nests are more complex, consisting of two layers. The lower layer is used for the eggs, and the female utilizes the upper layer for shelter. She remains with her eggs throughout incubation, which may last more than two months. Females defending their nests are reputedly bad-tempered and aggressive and will attack if someone ventures close to a nest. This snake rears up and spreads an impressive hood, the head sometimes more than 1 m (3 ft) off the ground. Males are said to remain in the vicinity of the nest and also protect the eggs. When the eggs hatch, the young move off and have to fend for themselves.

GREEN MAMBA
Dendroaspis angusticeps

The Black Mamba is an African snake, occurring from Senegal and Kenya south into southern Africa, where it is found in savanna and open bush. This graceful, alert, and unpredictable snake, with its deadly venom, is undoubtedly one of the most feared snakes in the world. Though it averages 3 m (10 ft) in length, it may exceed 4.5 m (15 ft) and is, after the King Cobra of Asia, the longest venomous snake in the world. It is active during the day and hunts its prey. This is often done from a permanent lair, to which it will return regularly if not disturbed. It is also fond of basking and may return to a suitable site daily. If it senses danger, it will merely slither away into dense undergrowth or down the nearest hole. Although equally at home in trees and on the ground, it shows a marked preference for the latter.

The Black Mamba is a large snake and can move comfortably with as much as a third of its body off the ground. The maximum speed of the Black Mamba, and most other snakes for that matter, is grossly exaggerated, and it is unlikely that this snake is capable of exceeding 20 km/h (12.5 mi/h).

The Black Mamba is not aggressive but extremely nervous and, like most snakes, prefers to move off when disturbed. If cornered it will gape, exposing the dark interior of the mouth, and spread a narrow hood while waving the tongue slowly up and down. Any sudden movement at this stage will be met with a series of rapid strikes, often with fatal results. Mamba venom is neuro-

toxic and quick-acting.

The Green Mamba occurs from East Africa to South Africa, favoring coastal regions and forests. It is strictly tree-living and is very shy, quickly disappearing into its leafy environment if disturbed.

BLACK MAMBA
Dendroaspis polylepis

EASTERN CORAL SNAKE

Micrurus fulvius fulvius

100

This snake, with its distinct bright black, red, and yellow bands, is found from Florida north to North Carolina, and west to Mississippi and eastern Louisiana. It may be found near streams, ditches, in open woodland, pine woods, or dry, open, bushy areas. Coral snakes are thought to be active only at night but spend much of their time hunting for food during the day. This is done by probing among leaf litter and rotting vegetation. They feed on small snakes, lizards, and, occasionally, nestling rodents. The Eastern Coral Snake spends its time hidden under fallen logs, beneath leaf litter, or even in tortoise burrows. Females, averaging 50 cm (2 ft) in length, lay four to seven eggs but may lay as many as thirteen. This snake is preyed upon by other snakes, predatory birds, and even the bullfrog. The Eastern Coral Snake is poisonous and has short fangs in the front of the mouth. It seldom attempts to bite and hides its head beneath coils when confronted. Even if it does bite, its mouth is very small, making it quite difficult for the snake to deliver a full bite. Its venom attacks the nervous system, often causing severe pain at the site of the bite. Such a bite could be fatal if not treated.

The Cape Coral Snake is found from Angola south into Namibia and South Africa, where it frequents a variety of habitats, including dry or sandy soil, savanna, or open woodland. It is a small, stocky snake, averaging about 30 cm (1 ft), but can reach a length of 75 cm (2.5 ft). It spends its days in self-dug burrows, under rocks, or in rock crevices, emerging at dusk to seek food. It preys on lizards, small snakes, and small rodents. It is an irascible snake that will rear and spread a narrow hood if disturbed. It also hisses and will strike repeatedly, lunging forward. Because it spreads a narrow hood, it is also called the Coral Cobra. The female lays three to eleven eggs in summer. Very little is known of the venom of this snake, but it is believed to be dangerously neurotoxic.

CAPE CORAL SNAKE
Aspidelaps lubricus

SHIELD-NOSE SNAKE

Aspidelaps scutatus

The Shield-nose Snake is found in parts of Namibia, Botswana, Zimbabwe, Mozambique, and northern South Africa. Its preferred habitats include savanna and sandy plains. This snake is similar in habits to the Cape Coral Snake, hiding during the day and foraging for food at night. It preys on small rodents, amphibians, lizards, and snakes. The Shield-nose Snake is easily identified by the prominent scale on its nose, which it uses as a "bulldozer." It is usually sluggish but very active after summer rains. Like some other snakes, it may pretend to be dead, but when molested performs like the Cape Coral Snake, lifting its head off the ground, striking and hissing furiously. It does not spread a hood. The female, measuring about 45 cm (1.5 ft) in length, is egg-laying. Though no human deaths resulting from the bite of this snake have been recorded to date, the venom is thought to be dangerous.

COMMON DEATH ADDER

Acanthophis antarcticus

The Death Adder is found in Australia, except for the desert regions and the extreme southeast, and in New Guinea and adjacent islands. It is adder-like both in appearance and in habits, and possesses a highly toxic venom that can kill a human. Its preferred habitats include sandy soil or grassy plains, where it spends a great deal of the day half buried. It is active at night and, like many true adders, relies on cryptic coloration to avoid detection. This snake uses the tip of its tail to lure its prey—the brightly colored tail tip is wriggled about to resemble an insect. Any creature that is drawn close in this manner is seized. The Death Adder strikes quickly from a coiled position. It preys on small mammals, birds, and, occasionally, lizards. It averages 50 cm (2 ft) in length, with a maximum length of 1 m (3 ft). Females are live-bearing, producing up to twenty young at a time. This snake has reached an interesting evolutionary stage in that it resembles an adder with its short, stocky body and triangular head, but it is an elapid with large, fixed fangs situated in the front of the mouth. The

Death Adder is one of the most dangerous venomous snakes in Australia and possesses an extremely toxic venom.

PUFF ADDER

Bitis arietans

The Puff Adder is Africa's most common venomous snake and is found throughout Africa south of the Sahara and in Arabia and Yemen. It is found in most habitats except for true deserts and tropical rain forests. Though somewhat sluggish and slow-moving, this bad-tempered and excitable snake can strike suddenly and swiftly. The Puff Adder is primarily a ground-dweller but may venture onto low shrubs and bushes to bask, especially after heavy rains, when the ground is wet. Basking takes place in the early morning or late afternoon. It is active at night. In many areas it rests on tarred roads in the evenings after warm days to absorb warmth, and many snakes are killed by vehicles. Puff Adders rely on perfect camouflage and immobility to escape

detection and are responsible for many serious snakebite incidents throughout their range, with people stepping onto or close to concealed snakes. They seldom move off and normally strike from a concealed position, before which they may emit a hissing or puffing sound, hence the common name. Progression is slow and caterpillarlike, with the snake relying almost entirely on its ventral scales, unless agitated, when it will move off in the normal snakelike manner. Most snakes swim well, and the Puff Adder is no exception. It swims on the surface with undulating movements of the body. This snake shows wide color variation, from bright yellow with black chevrons to dull gray with brown chevrons. Striped individuals, like the one on the right, have been found in recent years. The venom of the Puff Adder is potently cytotoxic, attacking tissue and blood cells. Symptoms may include extreme pain with swelling and large blisters in the region of the bite. Fortunately, the venom is slow-acting, taking a day or longer to cause death if not treated. The fangs of this snake are very large, measuring up to 2 cm (.8 in) in length.

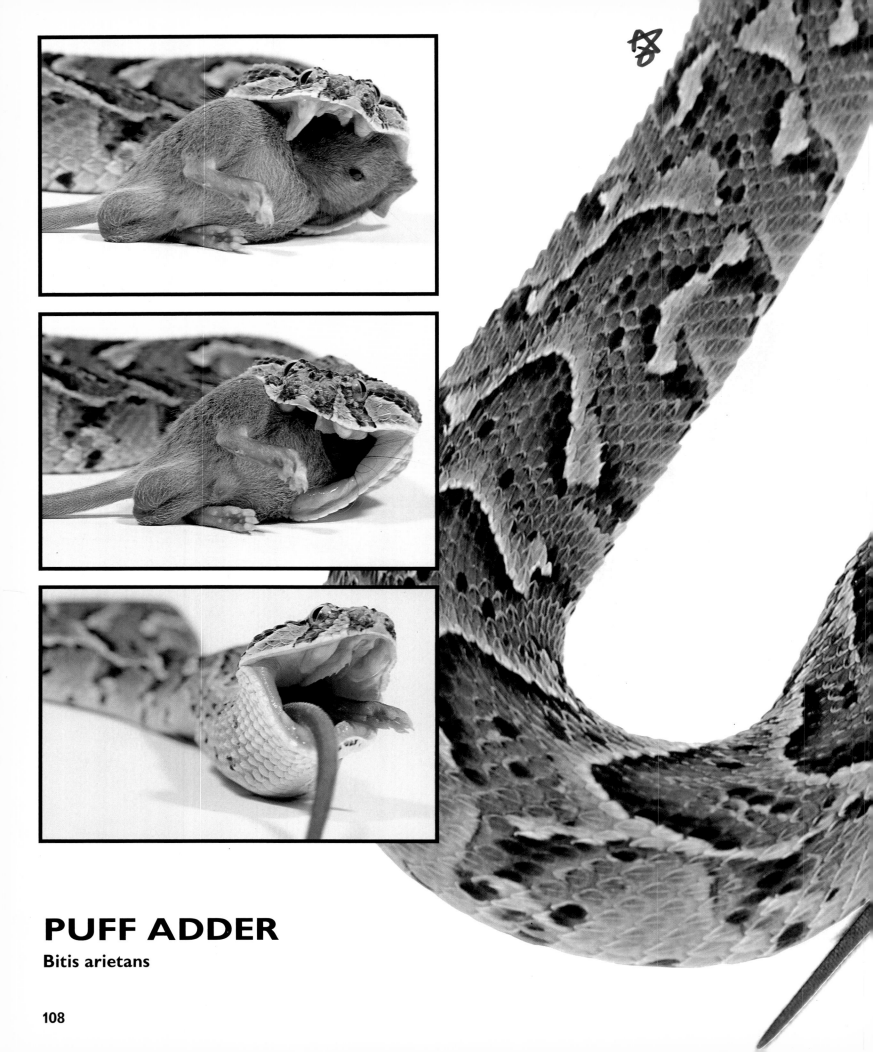

PUFF ADDER

Bitis arietans

Enemies of the Puff Adder, other than humans, include birds of prey, warthogs, some mammals, monitor lizards, and other snakes. The Puff Adder preys upon rats, mice, and other small terrestrial mammals, although ground-living birds, lizards, and toads may also be taken. The snake usually ambushes its prey. It strikes very quickly and may hang on to its prey. More often, it will merely inject sufficient venom to kill its prey when striking and not hang on. Thereafter, it follows the scent of its prey, and once the prey is located it is inspected with flicking tongue. The snake may take its prey into its mouth several times before locating its head. It then slowly swallows the prey whole, using one fang at a time to draw the animal into its mouth. Such a feeding session could last up to one hour. In a warm environment it would take three to four days for the food to be digested, whereafter the opportunistic snake will patiently await the arrival of its next meal.

The female gives birth to twenty to forty young, though exceptional litters of eighty or more have been reported. The young, each measuring 15 to 20 cm (6 to 8 in) in length, are born in a fine membranous sac, from which they break free after a few twists and turns. Large individuals from East Africa have reportedly produced as many as 150 young in a single litter, the most for any snake species in the world.

GABOON VIPER

Bitis gabonica

This colorful snake, the largest of all African adders, is confined to the moist, thickly wooded forest regions and adjacent wooded areas from southern Sudan and Zaire south to northern Zululand in South Africa. Its bizarre markings blend well with the background vegetation, making it extremely difficult to detect. Though primarily active at night, it will often bask in a patch of sunlight on the forest floor. Compared with the Puff Adder, it is surprisingly placid in nature unless molested or closely approached, when it will emit a series of long, drawn-out hisses with the forepart of the body raised off the ground. It strikes only as a last resort or if stepped on. Despite its sluggishness, the Gaboon Viper can strike with lightning speed. It may hunt actively from dusk onward or otherwise lie and wait to ambush its prey. Unlike most other adders, this snake is inclined to hang on to its prey until the venom takes effect. Prey includes rodents, hares, small monkeys, ground-living birds, and toads. The female gives birth to between sixteen and thirty young but may produce as many as sixty. Gaboon Viper venom is cytotoxic and comparable with that of the Puff Adder. However, much larger quantities are injected. The fangs of this snake may reach 5 cm (2 in) in length and can penetrate deeply into flesh. Fortunately, bites are rare. A full bite from this snake will result in alarming symptoms and early death unless treated promptly with antivenin.

This is one of the most colorful snakes in the world and is found from Kenya and Uganda to Sudan in the north and through Zaire to Guinea in the west. It favors damp or even aquatic environments and is found in swamps, forests, and marshes, where it is most active at night. Despite its coloration, it is very well cam- ouflaged. The Rhinoceros Viper feeds on mammals, which it ambushes, and is also known to take frogs, toads, and fish. The female is live-bearing, producing about twenty-five but some- times as many as forty young at a time. Like the Gaboon Viper, this species possesses a highly toxic venom that could prove fatal to humans. Adults average just over 1 m (3 ft) and reach a maximum length of close to 2 m (7 ft).

RHINOCEROS VIPER
Bitis nasicornis

EUROPEAN ADDER
Vipera berus

Occurring from the British Isles throughout Europe except for the south, then north to the Arctic Circle through the former Soviet Union and northern China to the Pacific coast, the European Adder has the widest distribution of any snake in the world. It is also the only venomous snake in Britain and northern Europe and the only snake to be found in the Arctic Circle. It occurs in a variety of habitats, such as open woodland, grassy hillsides, marshes, moors, and swamps, but not in dense woodland. Sometimes found in colonies, the presence of this snake depends upon the availability of suitable hibernating sites, basking spots, and a supply of food. It is active during the day, when it may hunt for food; otherwise, it awaits its prey in ambush. The prey, consisting of lizards, small mammals, and fledgling and nestling birds, is struck and left to die, as with most adders. Once the venom has taken effect, the snake will follow the scent of its prey by flicking its tongue. Once located, the meal is leisurely swallowed headfirst. Though venomous and dangerous, this snake rarely causes human fatalities. During mating there is often combat between males as they compete for females. They wrestle until the loser retreats. They do not bite one another during combat. The female produces between four and twelve live young. Adults average 45 cm (1.5 ft) but may reach almost 1 m (3 ft).

very quickly and is dangerously venomous. This snake is most active at night but may be seen during the day, especially during warmer weather. It feeds on small mammals, such as mice, snakes, lizards, and birds, while the young prey heavily on lizards. Warm-blooded prey are struck but not seized, and left to die from the effect of the venom. The snake then follows the scent of the animal and will swallow it headfirst. Like all snakes it has many enemies, including predatory birds, polecats, and even wild boars. Adults average 60 cm (2 ft) in length, with a maximum length of nearly 1 m (3 ft). The female is live-bearing, producing four to fifteen young. The Long-nose Viper is not an aggressive snake and will usually slither off and hide if disturbed; otherwise, it may hiss. When it strikes, it does so quickly and effectively. Its venom is potentially lethal to humans, and a victim will re-quire urgent medical help.

The Long-nose Viper is the largest and most dangerous viper on the European mainland and occurs from southwestern Europe to southwestern Asia. Throughout most of its range it avoids moist localities, favoring dry brushy and rocky hillsides and the drier parts of the Balkan region. It is often found in stony hills and where there are stone walls, but prefers areas where vegetation is sparse. It may also be found in forest clearings. This snake is fond of basking, often coiling on top of rocks or climbing onto shrubs or low branches of trees. It favors sunny slopes. The Long-nose Viper is a slow and clumsy snake and is less inclined to bite than the European Viper. It can strike

LONG-NOSE VIPER

Vipera ammodytes

PERINGUEY'S VIPER

Bitis peringueyi

This small adder, averaging 20 to 25 cm (8 to 10 in) with a maximum length of 30 cm (1 ft), is found in southern Angola and Namibia, where it inhabits the soft, windblown dunes of the west coast. It is well-known for its ability to side-wind—the only effective way for a snake to negotiate the soft, unstable dune sand. Only two sections of the body touch the dune sand at any one time. A section of the body is virtually thrown sideways, followed by the next section. A major advantage is that most of the body does not make contact with the hot sand while moving. The snake buries itself in the sand to escape the heat of the day and to ambush its prey.

When buried, it leaves the top of its head, its eyes, and the tip of its tail exposed. The tail is supposedly used to attract lizards. Once a lizard is spotted, the black-tipped tail is wriggled as a lure to imitate an insect. When the lizard dashes forward to grab it, it is seized by the snake. The eyes of this snake are well adapted and are situated on top of the head. The snake drinks the water that collects on its body when fog moves in from the cold Atlantic Ocean. The female is live-bearing, giving birth to between three and ten minute young in late summer. The venom of this snake is slightly cytotoxic and may cause pain and local swelling.

WESTERN DIAMONDBACK RATTLESNAKE

Crotalus atrox

This snake is found from northern Mexico north through Texas to Arkansas, and west to southeastern California. It is a large snake, averaging 1.3 m (4 ft) but often exceeding 2 m (7 ft) in length. The Western Diamondback Rattlesnake is found in dry and semiarid areas, including brushy plains, canyons, deserts, and open forest. Though most active at night, it may search for food in the early morning and late afternoon. It preys upon small mammals and birds. The female of this species produces four to twenty-five young at a time. If threatened, it may coil into a striking position, rattling its tail vigorously while the tongue slowly flicks up and down. It strikes quickly and effectively, and has a highly toxic venom that may result in human fatalities if not treated. Bites are quite common. This snake hibernates in winter, and up to one hundred individuals may hibernate together.

URACOAN RATTLESNAKE

Crotalus vegrandis

This little-known rattle-snake is confined to the state of Monogas in Venezuela, South America. It is smaller than the Neotropical Rattlesnake, averaging 1 m (3 ft) in length. The Uracoan Rattlesnake lives in dry savannas, dry forests, and thorn woodland, where it spends much of its time sheltering down armadillo burrows, under leaves or plant debris, in rock crevices, under fallen trees or cacti, or in other suitable refuges. It may emerge for short periods to bask. It is active from dusk onward, when it hunts for small mammals, birds, and, occasionally, large lizards. The vividly marked young feed on lizards, nestling rodents, and insects such as grasshoppers and crickets. The venom of this snake is extremely potent and potentially lethal to humans. A victim will require urgent medical care and, in all probability, large quantities of antivenin serum.

CASCABEL
Crotalus durissus

The Cascabel, also known as the Neotropical Rattlesnake, is found from southeastern Mexico south through much of Central America to Costa Rica. This species is by far the most dangerous of all the rattlesnakes. It is found in a variety of habitats, including dry to very dry forests, thorn scrub or woodland, rocky hills, dry open areas, pine-oak forests, palm savannas, natural breaks in cloud forests, forest clearings, and farmland. Occasionally, it is found in dense forests but is absent from rain forests. Individuals average about 1.2 m (4 ft) in length; the maximum length is 2 m (7 ft). The Cascabel is a stout and bad-tempered snake that is feared throughout its range. When confronted it puts up a dramatic display, drawing back into a springlike coil with up to half of its body well off the ground and its head held high while rattling its tail furiously. It carefully watches its adversary while flicking its tongue slowly, judging the striking distance. Bites from this snake constitute a significant proportion of snakebite deaths throughout its range, and victims require quick and effective treatment. Large quantities of antivenin serum may be required. A bite is often followed by a stinging pain, then a numb sensation at the site of the bite, followed by muscle pain, weakness, and vomiting. In some regions the venom may also affect the neck muscles, resulting in what has been described as the "broken neck" effect.

EASTERN DIAMONDBACK RATTLESNAKE
Crotalus adamanteus

A large rattlesnake averaging 1.2 m (4 ft) but reaching a length of 2.6 m (8.5 ft), the Eastern Diamondback Rattlesnake is found from the Florida Keys north into coastal North Carolina, and west to Mississippi and Louisiana. It lives in a variety of dryish habitats, where it seeks shelter in mammal or tortoise burrows, in hollow logs, or among exposed root systems. It is most active at dusk and dawn, when it actively hunts rabbits and other small mammals; otherwise, it awaits its prey in ambush. The female produces six to twenty-one young at a time. The venom of the Eastern Diamondback Rattlesnake is very potent and potentially fatal to humans. Urgent medical care is required if someone is bitten.

PYGMY RATTLESNAKE

Sistrurus miliarius

The Pygmy Rattlesnake is found from North Carolina south to the Florida Keys, and west to eastern Oklahoma and central Texas. It lives in open woodland, mixed pine-hardwood forests, marshes, and fields near swamps. Within these habitats it prefers dry sandy areas but is usually found close to water. It is active in the afternoon and early evening but may also be seen at other times of the day, depending on the temperature. When not active, it seeks refuge in mammal or tortoise burrows, under plant debris, or beneath fallen logs. The Pygmy Rattlesnake is fond of basking in the morning. It feeds on insects, mice, and other small mammals, snakes, lizards, frogs, toads, and nestling birds. It has many enemies, including indigo snakes, kingsnakes, coral snakes, predatory birds, opossums, skunks, and domestic cats. The biggest threat comes from habitat destruction; many snakes are killed by vehicles when crossing roads. The female usually produces six to eight minute young, the range being three to thirty-two young. Males are known to engage in combat by raising the foreparts of their bodies off the ground and pushing against one another. The snake that is pinned to the ground first untwists itself and slithers off in defeat. No attempt is made to bite while in combat. The venom of the Pygmy Rattlesnake causes severe pain and swelling but is unlikely to result in human fatalities. Medical help should be sought.

123

Also known as the Water Moccasin, this snake is found from south-western Virginia south to the Florida Keys, and west to southern Illinois, south Missouri, Oklahoma, and central Texas. It favors aquatic environments, such as brackish coastal marshes, lowland swamps, cypress swamps, lakes, rivers, ponds, and irrigation ditches. The Cottonmouth often basks in the day and is active at night. It feeds on fish, snakes, lizards, hatchling alligators, and even terrapins. The female produces up to sixteen live young at a time. When threatened it gapes, exposing the cotton-colored interior of its mouth, and it bites readily. The venom of this snake is very potent and potentially lethal to humans.

124

COTTONMOUTH

Agkistrodon piscivorus

JARARACA
Bothrops neuwiedi

The Jararaca occurs from Bolivia through Paraguay, Uruguay, and Argentina. It is a terrestrial pit viper and inhabits dry or rocky regions in savannas, thorn scrub, temperate forests, and tropical and semitropical deciduous forests. Adults average 70 cm (2 ft) in length but may reach 1.2 m (4 ft). It feeds on lizards and small mammals.

This species is highly venomous and is quick to strike. It features in many snakebite cases throughout its range, especially in the south. Victims require urgent medical care. Like many other South American species, very little is known about this snake, its distribution, and the effects of its venom.

EYELASH VIPER

Bothriechis schlegeli

Also known as the Palm Viper, this snake is found from the south of Mexico to Venezuela and Ecuador. The common name comes from small, horny scales above the eyes. It varies in color, from green or olive with black or reddish spots to yellow-green with brown spots and even nearly black. The individual on this page is unusually marked. The Eyelash Viper is strictly tree-living, usually coiling on a branch during the day. It is a nocturnal inhabitant of tropical moist forests, montane wet forests, or wet subtropical forests, where it feeds on lizards, frogs, small birds, and mammals. Captive individuals readily take mice. It averages 60 cm (2 ft) in length, with a maximum length of 80 cm (3 ft). It is widespread and abundant throughout most of its range and is often accidentally shipped overseas with bananas. The Eyelash Viper is quite aggressive and has very long fangs. It may strike with most of its body lunging forward while hanging on to a branch with its prehensile tail. Its venom is potent and potentially lethal.

Also known as the Sedge Viper, this snake is found in high-lying areas of central tropical Africa, adjacent western and southern Tanzania, and elsewhere in central Africa to Malawi and Zambia. Its color varies from bright green to olive or dark green, with irregular or zigzag black markings. The head has a black V shaped marking that may vary in size from snake to snake. The body scales are strongly ridged and overlap one another, while the head is rather large for the slender body. The African Bush Viper has a pre-hensile tail that is supposedly used as a lure to attract prey. The perfectly camouflaged snake wriggles the colorful tip of its tail to imitate an insect and lures frogs and lizards closer. It also feeds on rodents and birds and is known to rob birds' nests. The African Bush Viper is strictly arboreal; usually found in low bushes, it may also be found at heights exceeding 7 m (23 ft). It inhabits forest regions, includ-ing montane forests, upland swamplands, bushes along streams, and lake shores. It is nocturnal but is fond of basking during the day. This is one of the smaller bush vipers, averaging 30 to 40 cm (1 to 1.3 ft) with a maximum length of 70 cm (2 ft). The female is live-bearing. It is abundant throughout its range, but because of its excel-lent camouflage and inactivity during the day, it is seldom seen. Nothing is known of the venom or toxicity.

AFRICAN BUSH VIPER

Atheris nitschei

LOWLAND SWAMP VIPER

Atheris superciliaris

The Lowland Swamp Viper occurs from Mozambique up the Zambezi river to Lake Malawi and Tanzania. It inhabits low-lying swamps, marshes, and floodplains. It is a robust snake, averaging 40 cm (1.3 ft) but with a maximum length of just over 60 cm (2 ft). Males are the smaller of the sexes and seldom exceed 40 cm (1.3 ft) in length. Very little is known of this secretive snake. It is largely terrestrial, inhabiting rodent burrows during the day and emerging at dusk to hunt for frogs. Captive individuals readily feed on mice. The females are live-bearing, producing three to eight young at a time. The Lowland Swamp Viper is quite aggressive and quick to bite. It possesses a fairly potent venom. Little is known about the venom, but studies are continuing.

YELLOW-BELLIED SEA SNAKE

Pelamis platurus

Also known as the Pelagic Sea Snake, this is the most widely distributed sea snake in the world and is found throughout the warmer waters of the Indian and Pacific Oceans, from the eastern and southern coasts of Africa to the western coast of tropical America.

It is a truly pelagic, or ocean-going, snake that is usually a surface-dweller that tends to float motionless on the sea currents. It is an accomplished diver but prefers to stay on the surface, even when disturbed. It is usually associated with slicks that have been described as rivers in the ocean, where it is found among floating branches, coconuts, logs, and foam. The floating debris also attracts a variety of small fish, upon which it preys. These fish instinctively assemble beneath floating debris and may even assemble beneath floating Yellow-bellied Sea Snakes.

Like most sea snakes, the Yellow-bellied Sea Snake is specially adapted to its aquatic existence. With its laterally compressed body and paddle-shaped tail, it may even be mistaken for an eel. Its belly scales are greatly reduced, as they serve no purpose in the sea, and the vast majority of sea snakes are therefore awkward or helpless on land. It swims using lateral undulations, very much like a fast-moving snake on land. It is not aggressive but will attack if molested.

Adults average 40 to 60 cm (1.3 to 2 ft), with the males reaching 75 cm (2.5 ft) and the females 1 m (3 ft) in length. As it is an ocean-going snake, the female produces live young with between two and eight being born at a time.

Little is known about the venom of this snake, other than that it is potentially lethal. In parts of its range, like the southern coast of Africa, it is seldom seen. Some individuals, usually badly battered by rough seas, are washed ashore during heavy storms.

LAKE TAAL SNAKE

Hydrophis semperi

This unusual snake, also known as the Duhol, inhabits freshwater and is one of two sea snakes that do so. It is only found in Lake Taal, a landlocked lake in southern Luzon, and is endemic to the Philippines. Lake Taal is situated in an ancient volcanic crater, which still has a small active volcano. The lake is roughly 20 km (12.4 mi) in diameter and flows into the sea via a narrow, fast-flowing stream of about 10 km (6.2 mi). While many sea snakes are known to enter freshwater, only to return to the sea, the Lake Taal Snake never enters the sea. It is a small snake, averaging 50 cm (2 ft), with a maximum length of about 80 cm (3 ft). Little is known about this species, other than that it preys on fish, as do most members of the genus. The Lake Taal Snake is not heavily exploited by commercial fishermen, but is considered something of a delicacy among Asian people, largely because of its fatty body tissue.

ACALYPTOPHIS SEA SNAKE

Acalyptophis peronii

This surface-swimming sea snake inhabits waters adjacent to reefs but avoids shallow coral reef waters. It is found in seas between northern Australia and southern New Guinea, where it is often seen at night. The head and neck area is thinner than the rest of its body, allowing it to lunge forward underwater in order to catch its prey. It feeds on eels and fossorial fish. Adults average 1 m (3 ft) in length, and the female gives birth to between eight and ten young at a time. It is a placid snake that seldom attempts to bite.

HARDWICKE'S SEA SNAKE

Lapemis hardwickii

Hardwicke's Sea Snake occurs throughout southeast Asia, from the Bay of Bengal eastward to the coast of the Malay Peninsula and north to Japan, through Indonesia and the Philippines, to New Guinea and Australia. It is common throughout most of its range, where it favors silted estuaries, reef water, and shallow, clear coastal water. It is abundant in shallow estuaries along the coasts of Vietnam, Malaysia, and the Philippines, especially during the rainy season from July to November.

It is usually olive to greenish or yellowish above, with a series of dark crossbars that are much wider than the light background color, and pale cream to yellowish on the belly. The broadened tail is barred with a black tip. Adults average 70 cm (2 ft) in length but may exceed 1 m (3 ft). Adult males have thornlike scales along the lower sides of the body.

This snake is not a specialized feeder and preys on a wide variety of species. It may feed on pelagic prey, or fish from the sand-reef interphase, or even nocturnal fish, which it takes during the day while they are asleep. Like some of the other sea snakes, it stalks its prey cautiously and then lunges forward.

Hardwicke's Sea Snake is often netted in waters 20 to 30 m (66 to 98 ft) deep and has been observed in water up to 40 m (131 ft) deep. In parts of its range it is the dominant snake species captured during trawling for fish. Fishermen regard such snakes tangled in their nets as pests and freely handle them when untangling them. Though thought to be relatively inoffensive, many fishermen are bitten in the process, sometimes with fatal results. Scientists regard this species as one of the most dangerous of the sea snakes.

YELLOW-LIPPED SEA SNAKE

Laticauda colubrina

The Yellow-lipped Sea Snake is found in the coastal waters of New Guinea and the Pacific islands, through southeast Asia to Japan. It is a smooth-scaled snake that favors shallow waters around reefs, lagoons, and mangrove swamps. Though most active at night, it may be found basking on rocks, coral reefs, or in mangrove swamps at low tide.

Unlike most sea snakes, the Yellow-lipped Sea Snake spends a great deal of its time on land, sheltering in caves, crevices, or among rocks, sometimes very far from water. It does, however, feed in water. It preys upon a variety of fish and eels. Adults average around 1 m (3 ft) in length, and the females grow larger than the males.

It lays eggs on land, in crevices or in caves, and thousands of individuals may congregate on beaches during the breeding season. This species is heavily exploited in the Philippines for its skin and meat, and some people believe that if you consume its gall bladder, your vision improves. Tens of thousands of these snakes are killed every year, and it is estimated that more than 10,000 snakes can be taken from Gato Island in the Philippines in a single year! The trade in snake skins is enormous and poses a major threat to the survival of many snakes throughout the world.

The Yellow-lipped Sea Snake is blue to blue-gray in color, with between twenty and sixty-five black crossbars that encircle the body. The snout and upper lip are yellow, hence the common name. Like many sea snakes, it has a paddle-shaped tail which also has black crossbars. Its venom is highly toxic, but it only injects small quantities at a time. Few people are bitten by this inoffensive snake.

WALO WALO

Hydrophis belcheri

Walo Walo is a local name and is not used universally. This snake is found in Indo-Malaysian waters and the waters of New Guinea. It is completely aquatic and, like the Yellow-bellied Sea Snake, never comes ashore unless washed up during storms. The Walo Walo has a narrow body with a very long neck and tiny head.

Adults average 1 m (3 ft) but may reach 2.1 m (7 ft) in length and can be identified by about sixty dark crossbars on the body—these fade toward the belly. Females bear live young out at sea. It feeds on a variety of fish and is known to take fish from the nets of fishermen. Thousands are caught on hooks or in the nets of fishermen every year. The snakes bite viciously when captured, and there are many reports of fishermen's being bitten while untangling nets or taking such snakes off hooks. Some of these bites are fatal. The Walo Walo is also exploited for its skin and meat in the Philippines.

INDEX

BIBLIOGRAPHY

Ashton, R. E., Jr., & P. S. Ashton. 1981. *Handbook of reptiles and amphibians of Florida. Part 1: The snakes.* Windward. 176 pp.

Bauchot, R. (Ed.) 1994. *Snakes. A natural history.* Sterling. 220 pp.

Behler, J. L., & F. W. King. 1979. *The Audubon Society field guide to North American reptiles and amphibians.* Knopf. 743 pp.

Branch, B. 1988. *Bill Branch's field guide to the snakes and other reptiles of southern Africa.* Struik. 326 pp.

Brazaitis, P., & M. E. Watanabe. 1992. *Snakes of the world.* Crescent Books. 176 pp.

Breen, J. F. 1974. *Encyclopedia of reptiles and amphibians.* T.F.H. 576 pp.

Campbell, J. A., & W. W. Lamar. 1989. *The venomous reptiles of Latin America.* Comstock. 425 pp.

Carmichael, P., & W. Williams. 1991. *Florida's fabulous reptiles and amphibians.* World Publications. 120 pp.

Coborn, J. 1991. *The atlas of snakes of the world.* T.F.H. 591 pp.

Cogger, H. G. 1983. *Reptiles and amphibians of Australia.* Curtis Books. 660 pp.

Cox, M. J. 1991. *The snakes of Thailand and their husbandry.* Krieger. 526 pp.

Duellman, W. E. (Ed.) 1979. *The South American herpetofauna: Its origin, evolution, and dispersal.* Museum of Natural History, University of Kansas. 485 pp.

Dunson, W. A. (Ed.) 1975. *The biology of sea snakes.* University Park Press. 530 pp.

Ernst, C. H. 1992. *Venomous reptiles of North America.* Smithsonian Institution Press. 236 pp.

Frazer, D. 1983. *Reptiles and amphibians in Britain.* Collins. 254 pp.

Grzimek, B. 1984. *Grzimek's animal life encyclopedia.* Van Nostrand Reinhold. 588 pp.

Klauber, L. M. 1972. *Rattlesnakes: Their habits, life histories, and influence on mankind.* Volumes 1 & 2. University of California Press. 1,536 pp.

MacKay, A., & J. MacKay. 1985. *Poisonous snakes of eastern Africa and the treatment of their bites.* Author. 95 pp.

Marais, J. 1992. *A complete guide to the snakes of southern Africa.* Southern Book Publishers. 208 pp.

Markel, R. G. 1990. *Kingsnakes and milk snakes.* T.F.H. 144 pp.

McCoy, M. 1980. *Reptiles of the Solomon Islands.* Wau Ecology Institute. 80 pp.

Mehrtens, J. M. 1987. *Living snakes of the world in colour.* Sterling. 480 pp.

Minton, S. A., & M. R. Minton. 1971. *Venomous reptiles.* Allen & Unwin. 274 pp.

Minton, S. A., & M. R. Minton. 1973. *Giant reptiles.* Scribner's. 345 pp.

Phelps, T. 1981. *Poisonous snakes.* Blandford Press. 237 pp.

Ross, R. A., & G. Marzec. 1990. *The reproductive husbandry of pythons and boas.* Institute of Herpetological Research. 270 pp.

Russell, F. E. 1980. *Snake venom poisoning.* Lippincott. 562 pp.

Schmidt, K. P., & R. F. Inger. 1975. *Living reptiles of the world.* Doubleday. 287 pp.

Street, D. 1979. *The reptiles of North and Central Europe.* Batsford. 268 pp.

Tennant, A. 1984. *The snakes of Texas.* Texas Monthly Press. 561 pp.

Weidensaul, S. 1991. *Snakes of the world.* Apple Press. 128 pp.

PHOTOGRAPHIC CREDITS

Except for the photographs listed beneath, all photographs were taken by the author.

Rick Mathews: 7; Peter Dawson: 8; Eve by Lucas Cranach the Elder (1472–1553), Germany, Musée Royal des Beaux-arts, Anvers. Giraudon: 9; Bill Love, Glades Herpetofauna, Inc.: 11, 16, 19, 28, 29 (top); Anthony Bannister, Anthony Bannister Photo Library: 14 (top left), 15 (right), 22, 23 (top); Rod Patterson, Anthony Bannister Photo Library: 23 (bottom); William Holmstrom: 39; Dr. Bill Branch: 135; Dr. Sherman Minton: 136, 137, 139, 140, 141; Wayne Van Deventer: 138.